ENCYCLOPEDIA of
SHARKS

First published in 2010
by Igloo Books Ltd
Cottage Farm
Sywell
NN6 0BJ
www.igloo-books.com

A copy of the British Library Cataloguing-in-Publication Data is available from the British Library.

B044 0810

10 9 8 7 6 5 4 3 2 1

ISBN 978 1 84852 981 6

Author: Sally Morgan
Packaged by A&E Creative www.a-e-creative.com

Printed in China

ENCYCLOPEDIA of SHARKS

igloo

CONTENTS

WHAT ARE SHARKS?

WHAT ARE SHARKS?

Sharks are fish, and they come in many shapes and sizes. Some people fear going into the water because of sharks, but only a few are dangerous. The majority of sharks are small and completely harmless. Sharks are found in all the world's oceans, in warm and cold water, and in shallow and deep water.

NEW SPECIES

No one is exactly sure of the number of species of sharks in the oceans, as new species are being discovered all the time. Just 15 years ago, there were about 360 species, but now there are more than 400, and this figure may rise to 500 as scientists explore the deep ocean.

FINS AND GILLS

Sharks belong to the cartilaginous group of fish. This is because their skeleton is made of cartilage, the flexible material found in your nose and ears, rather than bone, which can break easily. Sharks are adapted to life in the water, with gills and fins.

THE IUCN RED LIST

The IUCN (International Union for Conservation of Nature) publishes the Red List. This is a list of all the animals and plants that are under threat of becoming extinct. There are a number of categories, depending on the numbers remaining and how quickly their numbers are declining. The categories are:

extinct
none remaining

extinct in the wild
only survives in captivity

critically endangered
greatest risk of becoming extinct in the wild

endangered
risk of becoming extinct in the wild

vulnerable
lower risk of becoming extinct in the wild

near threatened
likely to become endangered

least concern
lower risk of becoming endangered

data deficient
scientists do not have enough information

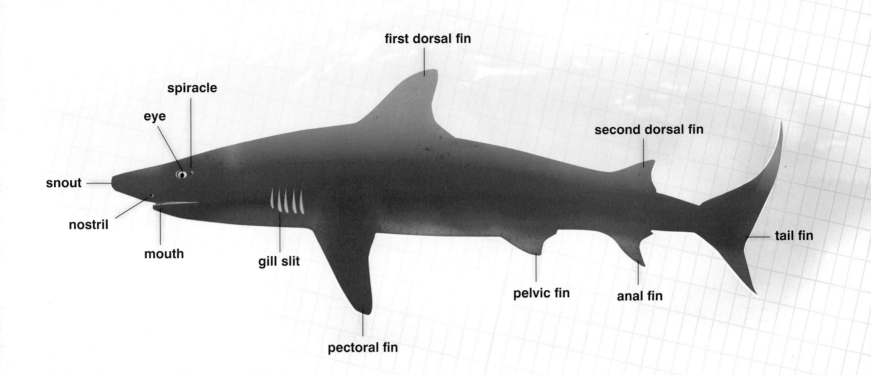

first dorsal fin

spiracle

eye

second dorsal fin

snout

nostril

tail fin

mouth

gill slit

pelvic fin

anal fin

pectoral fin

Water passes through their gills, where the oxygen is removed, and then out through their gill slits. Most sharks have five gill slits on each side of their head, but a few have six or seven. The skin of fish, such as the herring, is covered in scales, but a shark's skin is covered in tiny, toothlike structures called denticles. These denticles make the shark's skin feel rough, like sandpaper.

Sharks have two dorsal fins on their back, a pair of pectoral fins behind their head, a pair of pelvic fins toward their tail, and an anal fin on their underside, just in front of their tail. The tail itself ends in a large fin with two lobes. The shape, size, and color of the fins help scientists identify the different species, or types, of sharks.

In this book you will read about the lives of many different types of sharks. You will learn how to identify them, where they are found, and what they eat. You will also learn about their conservation status, meaning whether they are on the IUCN Red List or not.

▼ A shark's pectoral fins often look like wings, sticking out of the sides of its body.

ANGEL SHARK

The angel shark has a flattened body and looks more like a ray than a shark. It gets its name from the way in which its fins stick out of the sides of its body and look like wings.

SHARK FILES

COMMON NAME: Pacific angel shark, also called monkfish

LATIN NAME: Squatina californica

LENGTH: The Pacific angel shark grows to 4.9 ft. (1.5m), but other species can grow to 6.5 ft. (2m)

WEIGHT: 55 - 66 lbs. (25 - 30kg)

DIET: Fish, especially flatfish, crustaceans, and mollusks, such as squids

STATUS: Near threatened

MUST KNOW: Angel sharks are often called sand devils because they hide in the sand, and if divers swim too close, the sharks give them a nasty bite.

▼ The mottled brown and gray colors of the angel shark are the perfect camouflage on the seabed.

SNATCHED MEALS

There are more than 16 types of angel sharks, including the Pacific angel shark. Angel sharks live close to the seabed. During the day, they bury themselves in the mud and sand and wait for prey to pass close by. When prey comes within reach, the shark leaps forward with great speed and snatches it in its strong jaws. The shark's long, needle-like teeth are perfect for gripping slippery fish.

At night, the sharks come out of hiding and swim slowly over the seabed in search of prey. The Pacific angel sharks prey on squids during the winter months, but they also hunt mackerel, lizardfish, and shrimp.

REPRODUCTION

Female Pacific angel sharks are pregnant for about ten months. In the late spring and early summer the females swim into shallow water that is less than 295 ft. (90m) deep, where they give birth to up to 11 pups, each about 10 in. (25cm) long. The young sharks stay in shallow water until they are large enough to be safe from predators. Only one in every five pups is likely to survive to adulthood. The young reach maturity when they are about 31 in. (80cm) long and between 8 and 13 years old. Some live to 35 years of age.

APPEARANCE

The angel shark's body is flattened from top to bottom. The large pectoral and pelvic fins extend out to the sides. There are two small dorsal fins close to the tail. Its eyes are on the top of its head, and its gills are on the bottom. Its mouth is at the front of its broad snout.

WHERE IN THE WORLD...

Angel sharks can be found around the world to depths of up to 4,265 ft. (1,300m). The Pacific angel shark lives in the eastern Pacific Ocean, from Alaska to Chile.

Arctic Ocean

NORTH AMERICA

U.S.A.

Pacific Ocean

Atlantic Ocean

EUROPE

ASIA

AFRICA

SOUTH AMERICA

Indian Ocean

AUSTRALIA

Blue areas show where these sharks may be found.

▲ The angel shark has small barbels on its mouth that can taste the ground.

SHARK BITES

The main predators of the angel shark are larger sharks, such as the great white shark.

BAMBOO SHARK

There are several types of bamboo sharks, all of which are harmless to people. One of the most common is the white-spotted bamboo shark, a secretive shark found on coral reefs.

SHARK BITES

In 2002, a white-spotted bamboo shark in an aquarium in the U.S.A. laid some eggs that hatched into young sharks. Nothing strange about that, but this female had not been close to a male shark for six years!

WHERE IN THE WORLD...

The white-spotted bamboo shark is found in the Indian and Pacific oceans, along the coast from India to Japan. They are most common in Southeast Asia, where they are found on coral reefs.

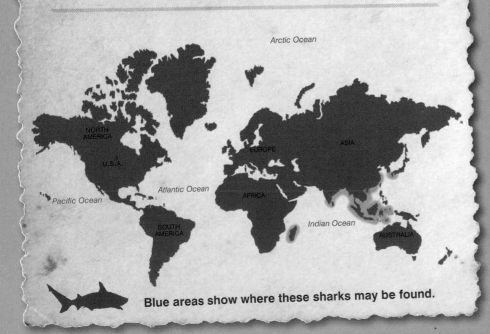

Arctic Ocean

NORTH AMERICA

U.S.A.

EUROPE

ASIA

Atlantic Ocean

AFRICA

Pacific Ocean

SOUTH AMERICA

Indian Ocean

AUSTRALIA

Blue areas show where these sharks may be found.

NIGHT HUNTER

The white-spotted bamboo shark lives close to the seabed. It is a nocturnal shark, which means that it comes out at night to hunt. During the day, it hides in crevices in the coral reef. Its teeth are adapted for preying on animals that have a hard shell, such as clams and crabs.

When the shark grabs these animals, its teeth slip backward so the tips point into the mouth. This leaves a large, flat surface of tooth that the shark uses to crush the prey's shell. This protects the tip of the shark's teeth that would be easily damaged if the teeth bit down on such a hard surface.

◄ This white-spotted bamboo shark pup has just hatched from its egg case.

SHARK FILES

COMMON NAME: White-spotted bamboo shark
LATIN NAME: Chiloscyllium plagiosum
LENGTH: Up to 35-37 in. (90-95cm)
WEIGHT: 22 lbs. (10kg)
DIET: Invertebrates, such as crabs, shrimp, clams, and small fish found on the seabed
STATUS: Near threatened
MUST KNOW: These small sharks are popular with aquarists, and thousands are kept as pets.

REPRODUCTION

White-spotted bamboo sharks are egg-layers. Each week the female lays one or two eggs over a period of about three months. This is a total of about 25 eggs per year. Each egg is about 6 in. (15cm) long. The eggs lie on the seabed for between three to four months, and then they hatch into young sharks about 6 in. (15cm) long. These sharks are mature by the time they are 25.6 in. (65cm) long.

Bamboo sharks can swim to depths of 4,920 ft. (1,500m). They spend a lot of time resting on the seabed.

APPEARANCE

This shark has a long, slender body with strong pectoral fins that it uses to crawl over the surface of the seabed. Its body is dark brown with light brown bands and many small white spots. It has several short barbels attached to each one of its nostrils. Some albino white-spotted bamboo sharks have been hatched at SeaWorld in Florida.

BANDED CATSHARK

The banded catshark has a number of different names, including brown-spotted catshark and gray carpet shark. It's called a catshark because of the whisker-like barbels attached to its nostrils.

▼ **Banded catsharks live in coral reefs and rock pools to depths of 278 ft. (85m).**

STRANDED ON THE SHORE

The banded catshark lives on the seabed and in coral reefs and rock pools. It can live for up to 12 hours out of water, a useful adaptation as it is often stranded on the shore when the tide goes out. When this happens, it can survive in the damp, by staying under a rock until the tide returns.

This shark is under threat because it is frequently caught in fishing nets. It also suffers because dynamite fishing is destroying the coral reefs where it lives. Fishermen set off dynamite in the water, and the blast stuns large numbers of fish, which makes them easier to catch. These sharks are harmless and look attractive, so they are a very popular choice for aquariums. Many are caught in the wild for sale to specialist pet stores.

SHARK FILES

COMMON NAME: Banded catshark
LATIN NAME: Chiloscyllium punctatum
LENGTH: Grows to 39-49 in. (100-125cm), males are longer than females
WEIGHT: 22-33 lbs. (10-15kg)
DIET: Invertebrates, such as worms, shrimp, and slow-moving fish on the seabed
STATUS: Near threatened
MUST KNOW: You can tell the male from the female by the claspers on the males. These are found under the anal fins.

▲ The distinctive bands of this shark are only visible in youngsters. As they grow into adults, the bands start to fade.

REPRODUCTION

These sharks lay long, flat egg cases that are about 6 in. (15cm) long by 4 in. (11cm) wide. The eggs are laid on the seabed and hatch after about three to four months. The young sharks are about 6 in. (15cm) long. Banded catsharks live for about 25 years.

APPEARANCE

The banded catshark has a slender, snake-like body and long tail. Its two dorsal fins are both about the same size. Young sharks have bands of black, dark gray, and white. These bands fade as the shark gets older, and the adults are a light brown color all over.

WHERE IN THE WORLD...

The banded catshark is a common species found in the Indo-Pacific Ocean, from India to North Australia and as far north as Japan.

Arctic Ocean

NORTH AMERICA

U.S.A.

Pacific Ocean

Atlantic Ocean

EUROPE

ASIA

AFRICA

SOUTH AMERICA

Indian Ocean

AUSTRALIA

Blue areas show where these sharks may be found.

BASKING SHARK

▼ A basking shark can filter up to 2,200 tons of water in just one hour – that's a lot of water!

The basking shark is the second-largest shark. It gets its name from the way it lies on the surface of the water, often rolled on its side, as if it were sunbathing. Its Latin name means "marine monster with large nose."

BIG MOUTH

The basking shark looks pretty scary as it swims along with its huge mouth wide open, but it is harmless. It may be one of the world's biggest sharks, but it feeds on some of the smallest animals and plants in the ocean – plankton. To feed, it simply opens its mouth as it swims along and water rushes in. The water passes from its mouth through its gills and out through its gill slits. Hanging in front of the gills are long, finger-like projections called gill rakers. These are similar to combs, and they remove all the food from the water. The shark only closes its mouth to swallow the food.

Each year, basking sharks swim thousands of miles. Some make regular journeys, or migrations. In the fall, they dive to depths of up to 2,950 ft. (900m) and swim south to warmer waters. They swim back in the spring.

REPRODUCTION

Little is known about the reproduction of the basking shark. The females may be pregnant for as long as three years. One known female gave birth to five pups, between 0.5-0.7 in. (1.5-1.8cm) long.

SHARK FILES

COMMON NAME: Basking shark
LATIN NAME   Cetorhinus maximus
LENGTH: Largest ever was 40 ft. (12.27m), but most are between 19-26 ft. (6-8m) long
WEIGHT: Can weigh up to 20 tons, but most are about 5 tons.
DIET: Plankton, small crustaceans, fish eggs, and small fish
STATUS: Vulnerable
MUST KNOW: Their liver is huge and rich in oil. It makes up a quarter of their weight.

Young basking sharks grow incredibly slowly and are not ready to breed until they are 12 to 16 years old.

APPEARANCE

The basking shark has a huge mouth that is about 3ft. (1m) wide, with five gill slits that almost encircle its entire head. Its teeth are small, just a few millimeters long, and its body is dark brown to blue-gray in color. Young basking sharks have a long, pointed snout that is hooked.

SHARK BITES

Basking sharks may be seen on their own but they usually form small groups. Sometimes there may be as many as 100 sharks in a group.

WHERE IN THE WORLD...

The basking shark is found around the world, especially in coastal waters where temperatures range between 45–56°F (8–14°C). These are waters where there is a lot of plankton.

Arctic Ocean

NORTH AMERICA

EUROPE

ASIA

U.S.A.

Atlantic Ocean

AFRICA

Pacific Ocean

SOUTH AMERICA

Indian Ocean

AUSTRALIA

Blue areas show where these sharks may be found.

▼ Basking sharks swim slowly, at just 3 mph (5km/h), by moving their whole body from side to side.

BLACKNOSE SHARK

The blacknose shark gets its name from the black blotch on the tip of its snout. This small, fast-swimming shark belongs to the family of requiem sharks that includes the silky and bull sharks.

SHARK BITES

This is quite a daring shark as it will snatch food from the mouths of larger sharks such as the Caribbean reef shark.

▼ Blacknose sharks live in reefs and shallow water, although adults can be found to depths of 197 ft. (60m).

◄ The black tip on the nose of this juvenile blacknose shark can be clearly seen.

THREATENING DISPLAY

The blacknose is a harmless shark, but it often performs a threatening display when divers get too close. It hunches its back and raises its head in an attempt to look larger. Being small, it is preyed upon by larger sharks.

Blacknose sharks live together in schools, made up of individuals of the same age and sex. Often, blacknose sharks are seen in large schools swimming with other schools of fish such as anchovy and mullet.

REPRODUCTION

Female blacknose sharks are pregnant for about ten months. In the spring and summer, the females swim to coastal areas with shallow water, such as mangrove swamps. There, they give birth to between three and six pups, each about 16 in (40cm) long. The pups stay in the safety of the shallow water, feeding on fish, until they are larger, then they move into deeper water. Blacknose sharks grow fast, and they are mature and ready to breed at two years of age, when they are about 3.2 ft (1m) long. Females live for between 9 and 16 years; males only four to nine years.

Scientists have discovered that female blacknose sharks living in the Gulf of Mexico reproduce every year but those living in the colder waters of the north - west Atlantic only reproduce every other year.

WHERE IN THE WORLD...

The blacknose shark occurs in the subtropical waters of the western Atlantic, from south-east USA to Brazil and the Caribbean.

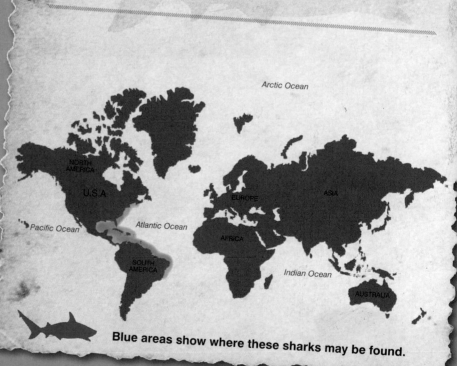

Blue areas show where these sharks may be found.

APPEARANCE

The blacknose shark has a streamlined shape, with a rounded snout and large eyes. Its color ranges from yellowish-brown to gray-green, with a yellowish-white underside. The tip of its second dorsal fin and the upper caudal lobe may be black.

17

SHARK TEETH

The first things people see when a shark opens its mouth are its teeth. Most sharks do not use their teeth to chew food. Instead, their teeth are designed to grip their prey and break the body into large chunks that they can swallow.

SHAPES AND SIZES

Shark teeth come in different shapes and sizes, depending on the type of prey that they hunt. Great whites and other sharks that hunt big prey, such as seals, have large, triangular teeth with sharp points and serrated edges. This is the ideal shape for gripping and cutting through the flesh of the prey animal.

▲ Sharks' jaws, such as these of the great white, are extremely powerful. Unlike any other animal, sharks can move their upper as well as their lower jaw.

Triangular-shaped teeth with sharp points for gripping prey, and serrated edges for slicing flesh.

Fish are slippery prey, so sharks that eat a lot of small fish, such as mackerel and anchovy, need teeth that can grip. The lemon shark has teeth that are shaped like needles to grip the slippery body of a fish.

Sharks that feed on snails, clams, sea urchins, and other animals with hard shells have teeth that are designed to crush and crunch.

The Port Jackson shark, for example, has broad teeth with a large, flat surface, which is ideal for crushing shells. Pointed teeth would not be of any use for feeding on animals with hard shells, and the shells would damage the points.

The plankton-feeding whale shark and basking sharks have hundreds of very small teeth.

An old tooth can be replaced in just 24 hours.

LOSING TEETH

The teeth of a shark are arranged in rows along the edge of the upper and lower jaws. Typically, a shark has up to five rows, with 30 teeth in each row, and the largest teeth in the front rows.

Shark teeth fall out all the time, as they are not attached to the jaw like human teeth. They are just buried in the gum. When one falls out, it is replaced by a tooth from the row behind, and a new tooth forms in the back row. As the shark grows, their teeth get larger, too. Sharks continue to replace teeth as they get older, so its lifetime a shark may have replaced thousands of teeth.

▲ The teeth of this mako shark do not have the serrated edges seen on the teeth of the great white.

USEFUL TEETH

People have long used shark teeth to make weapons, such as daggers, and tools to carve wood. In Hawaii, people made weapons that were edged with shark teeth, while shark-tooth tipped arrows have been found in South America.

BLACKTIP SHARK

This shark is called the blacktip because of the black tips of its fins. It belongs to the group of requiem sharks, and one of its closest relatives is the blacknose shark.

SHARK FILES

COMMON NAME: Blacktip shark
LATIN NAME: Carcharhinus limbatus
LENGTH: Usually about 5 ft. (1.5m), but the largest reported was 8.3 ft. (2.55m).
WEIGHT: About 44 lbs. (20kg)
DIET: Squids, crabs, shrimp, and fish, especially schooling fish, such as herring and sardines. It will also take fish found on the seabed and even small sharks and rays.
STATUS: Near threatened
MUST KNOW: The females return to the place where they were born to give birth to their pups.

▼ Blacktips are mostly found in coastal waters up to 100 ft. (30m) deep. But they have been found as deep as 200 ft. (60m).

SNAPPY HUNTERS

These fast-swimming sharks get very excited when they are hunting. They swim upward at great speed through a school of fish, snapping at any fish within reach. They are so fast that their speed often carries them out of the water. They spin several times in the air before crashing back into the water again.

Sometimes, blacktips jump out of the water and spin around in the air even when there is no food nearby. Scientists think that this may be to get rid of remoras or sharksuckers, small fish that attach themselves to sharks and cause them great irritation.

REPRODUCTION

The females swim into shallow water in bays and near mangrove swamps to give birth to as many as ten pups. The pups are about 15–28 in. (38–72cm) long. The pups stay in these nursery areas, where they are safe from predators, for several months before swimming out to sea. The sharks are mature at four to five years. They rarely live longer than 12 years.

APPEARANCE

The blacktip has a stout body with a long, narrow, pointed snout. Its skin is a dark gray to bronze on the back and white on its underside. It has a darker gray band running along each side, and the tips of its fins are black. The teeth in its upper jaw have large serrations, while those on the lower jaw are more finely serrated and curve inward.

WHERE IN THE WORLD ...

The blacktip shark has a wide distribution and can be found in the tropical and subtropical regions of the Atlantic, Indian, and Pacific oceans. They swim into bays, estuaries, and mangrove swamps.

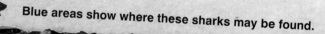

Blue areas show where these sharks may be found.

◄ The blacktip can be an aggressive shark and is considered dangerous to divers when there is food around.

SHARK BITES

Blacktips are responsible for almost 1 in 6 shark attacks that occur each year in the waters around Florida. Fortunately, the injuries are usually minor.

BLIND SHARK

The blind shark is not really blind. It gets its name from the way in which it pulls in its eyeballs so that its thick eyelids close when it is taken out of water. This gives the impression that it has no eyes.

SHARK BITES

Sometimes, a blind shark can be trapped in rock pools when the tide goes out, but this is not a problem, as it can survive for up to 18 hours out of water.

SUCKING UP FOOD

The blind shark is nocturnal, coming out at night to hunt for animals that live close to the seabed or on the coral reef. During the day, it hides in crevices and caves. It is a slow-moving shark that is harmless. When it finds prey, it vacuums it up using suction. This way, it can pull animals out of cracks in rocks.

Sometimes, the blind shark comes right up to the shore and can be seen in shallow rock pools, where it is barely covered by the water. However, it can live in deep water, too, and has been found at depths of 460 ft. (140m).

Blind sharks are usually harmless, but if they are annoyed by a diver, they may bite. They have been known to hang onto a diver's wetsuit, gripping the rubber firmly with their strong jaws.

WHERE IN THE WORLD ...

The blind shark is found in the western Pacific, along the east coast of Australia, from southern Queensland to the southern coast of New South Wales. It swims around rocky coasts, coral reefs, and in seagrass beds.

Arctic Ocean

NORTH AMERICA
U.S.A.
ASIA
EUROPE
Atlantic Ocean
AFRICA
Pacific Ocean
SOUTH AMERICA
Indian Ocean
AUSTRALIA

Blue areas show where these sharks may be found.

◀ **The blind shark moves slowly over the seabed in search of prey.**

SHARK FILES

COMMON NAME: Blind shark
LATIN NAME: Brachaelurus waddi
LENGTH: Up to 4 ft. (102m)
WEIGHT: About 22 lbs. (10kg)
DIET: Small fish, shrimp, crabs, squids, cuttlefish, and sea anemones
STATUS: Least concern
MUST KNOW: Its flesh has a strong taste of ammonia, so it is not fished for food, but it may become trapped in fishing nets.

REPRODUCTION

Female blind sharks give birth to up to eight pups, usually during the summer months. The pups are about 6–7 in. (15–18cm) long. Scientists think that these sharks reproduce every year, but they have not been widely studied.

The sharks are mature by the time they reach about 26 in. (65cm) in length. They are known to live for 20 years in captivity but probably have shorter lives in the wild.

APPEARANCE

This is a small shark with a stout body. It is brown with white spots, and sometimes there is a darker brown stripe along its body. Its underside is pale yellow with many small white spots. It has two dorsal fins of equal size placed far back toward it's tail. Long barbels hang from either side of its small mouth.

▼ **The blind shark belongs to the family of carpet sharks.**

BLUE SHARK

This is one of the easiest sharks to identify, as it is the only one that has a bright blue body. It is also one of the most dangerous, as it attacks people struggling in the water.

FEEDING FRENZY

The fast-moving blue shark swims long distances each year, moving from cooler to warmer waters with the seasons. Often large groups follow schools of small fish, such as anchovy, sardines, and herring. Large numbers of blue sharks are also often seen around the dead bodies of whales or dolphins floating in the water, biting at the flesh in a feeding frenzy.

Unfortunately, large numbers of blue sharks become entangled in drift nets. This is because they are attracted to the fish that are caught in the nets, and the sharks become entangled themselves. Scientists think that as many as 20 million may be killed each year, and for this reason the blue shark is at risk. Their meat is not used because it contains a lot of ammonia, so blue sharks are usually finned and their bodies tossed back into the ocean.

WHERE IN THE WORLD ...

The blue shark is believed to be one of the most widely distributed vertebrates. It is found around the world in both tropical and temperate waters. They prefer water temperatures of between 53–68°F (12–20°C) If the water is too warm, they swim to depths of up to 1,150 ft. (350m)

Arctic Ocean

NORTH AMERICA

U.S.A.

EUROPE

ASIA

Pacific Ocean

Atlantic Ocean

AFRICA

SOUTH AMERICA

Indian Ocean

AUSTRALIA

Blue areas show where these sharks may be found.

SHARK BITES

The largest litter of blue shark pups is believed to be 135!

▲ Blue sharks are often seen far out at sea. They are known to follow ships for several days, waiting for scraps to fall in the water.

REPRODUCTION

The female blue shark is pregnant for up to one year. The females give birth to a litter of between 25 and 50 pups. Each pup is about 18 in. (45cm) in length when it is born. Blue sharks grow fast and are ready to breed by the time they are four to six years of age. They live for up to 20 years.

APPEARANCE

These long, slim sharks are a deep indigo-blue color along their back with bright blue sides. Their undersides are white. Their eyes are large, and they have a long, cone-shaped snout that is longer than the width of their mouth. Their pectoral fins are particularly long and wing-like.

SHARK FILES

COMMON NAME: Blue shark
LATIN NAME: Prionace glauca
LENGTH: Mostly about 7.8–10 ft. (2.4–2.8m), but the largest ever recorded was 12 ft. (3.8m)
WEIGHT: Usually about 290–400 lbs. (130–180kg), but the largest weighed more than 440 lbs. (200kg)
DIET: Squids, cuttlefish, crabs, shrimp, fish, including small sharks, and even sea birds
STATUS: Near threatened
MUST KNOW: The skin of the female blue shark is three times thicker than that of the male because the males bite them during courtship.

BONNETHEAD SHARK

The bonnethead, or shovelhead, shark gets its name from the shape of its head. When viewed from above, its head looks like a spade or a shovel. It is related to the larger hammerhead sharks.

▼ The bonnethead prefers to stay close to shore, where there are coral reefs, shallow estuaries, and bays.

SMALL AND TIMID

The bonnethead is a small, timid shark that is found in groups of between 5 and 20 individuals. However, groups numbering hundreds and even thousands of individuals may be seen at certain times of year. They are seen on coral reefs in shallow coastal waters between 30–260 ft. (10–80m) deep.

HUNTING FOR FOOD

Many of the animals that the bonnethead hunts lie hidden in the mud. To find them, the shark uses its sense of electroreception to detect tiny electrical signals produced by animals. The bonnethead swims along the seabed, moving its head from side to side and scanning the mud for the signals that tell it an animal, such as a crab, is buried in the mud. The bonnethead's front teeth are small and sharp, ideal for gripping small prey such as fish. Its back teeth are broad and flat and are used to crush and grind the tough shell of its favorite food — crab.

SHARK FILES

COMMON NAME: Bonnethead shark
LATIN NAME: Sphyrna tiburo
LENGTH: About 3 ft. (1m), largest are just 5 ft. (1.5m)
WEIGHT: 22 lbs. (10kg)
DIET: Crustaceans, such as shrimp, crabs, mollusks, octopus, and small fish
STATUS: Least concern
MUST KNOW: The bonnethead is the only shark species in which the male and female look different. The females have a rounded head, while the males have a bulge at the front of their head.

REPRODUCTION

The female bonnethead gives birth to between 4 and 14 pups during the late summer and early fall. Each pup is about 14 in. (35cm) long.

APPEARANCE

The shark's head is broad and flattened, so its eyes are wide apart. It is gray or gray-brown in color, and sometimes there are small dark spots on its sides. Its first dorsal fin is tall, while the second one is much smaller and close to its tail. The pectoral fins are short.

▼ This shark uses its amazing sense of electroreception to find its prey. This is like a person using a metal detector to find objects in the ground.

WHERE IN THE WORLD . . .

The bonnethead occurs along the Atlantic and Pacific coasts of North and South America, from California to Ecuador and from North Carolina to southern Brazil. These sharks like warm water, so they swim south in the winter months.

Arctic Ocean

NORTH
AMERICA

ASIA

EUROPE

U.S.A.

Atlantic Ocean

AFRICA

Pacific Ocean

Indian Ocean

AUSTRALIA

SOUTH
AMERICA

Blue areas show where these sharks may be found.

SHARK BITES

The bonnethead is not as buoyant as many other sharks so if it stops moving it sinks in the water.

BULL SHARK

These bad-tempered sharks are among the most dangerous in the world, and they frequently attack people. They get their name from their aggressive nature and the way they head butt their prey.

SHARK BITES

Bull sharks can be found in the Mississippi River in North America and have been spotted as far north as St. Louis.

▼ Bull sharks are often mistaken for great white sharks. Both are very aggressive and have few predators.

SHARK FILES

COMMON NAME: Bull shark, also called whaler
LATIN NAME: Carcharhinus leucas
LENGTH: Males up to 6.5 ft. (2m), females up to 13 ft. (4m)
WEIGHT: Males grow to 220 lbs. (100kgs), females as much as 660lbs. (300kgs)
DIET: Dolphins, turtles, wading birds, other sharks, crustaceans, and mollusks
STATUS: Near threatened
MUST KNOW: Be careful at the water's edge, because bull sharks attack almost any animal in the water, even those that come to the water to drink.

▲ Bull sharks prefer shallow water, less than 100 ft. (30m) deep.

SMASH AND STUN

Bull sharks hunt alone. They swim slowly, using their excellent senses to locate their prey, even in the muddy water of rivers. Once they detect an animal, they charge forward at great speed and smash into the animal with their head. This stuns the animal, and the bull shark then takes a great bite out of them.

The males have a territory that they guard fiercely from other sharks, attacking any other animal that enters their space. But bull sharks are not without enemies. In Australia, crocodiles are known to attack them and young bull sharks may be hunted by tiger, sandbar, and even other bull sharks.

REPRODUCTION

Bull sharks are ready to breed when they are about ten years old. Female bull sharks are pregnant for up to ten months. The females travel to shallow coastal waters to give birth to 1 to 13 live pups. These places are called nurseries and are safe areas for the young sharks where there are few large predators. Each pup is about 28 in. (70cm) long. Female bull sharks live for about 16 years, while males only live for about 12 years.

WHERE IN THE WORLD ...

Bull sharks are usually found in the coastal waters of the tropics. They also live in fresh water, such as the Amazon River, in South America, the Brisbane River in Australia, and in the Zambezi River in Africa.

Blue areas show where these sharks may be found.

APPEARANCE

Bull sharks have a wide body, blunt head, and small eyes. They have large, triangular teeth with serrated edges. The upper part of their body is gray, and the underside is white. They have one large, triangular dorsal fin and a second, much smaller dorsal fin close to the tail.

SHARK SENSES

A lateral line runs down either side of the shark's body.

Sharks have amazing senses that allow them to detect and hunt prey. Their different senses work to help them track down prey, whether it is far away or buried in the mud.

Some sharks can see ten times better than a human can in dim light. All sharks also see in color, like humans.

SMELL

A shark's sense of smell is incredible. Scientists believe that some sharks could detect one drop of blood in an Olympic-size swimming pool and smell blood in the water from 1,312 ft. (400m) away. Sharks do this by using the paired nostril on their snout to taste water. Water flows into the nostril from both the right and the left side of the body and this helps the shark to figure out from which direction the smell is coming. Some sharks have whisker-like barbels hanging down from their nostrils. The sharks use these to feel and taste the seabed.

ELECTRORECEPTION

Sharks can detect the tiny electrical signals that all animals produce when they move. This is called electroreception. A shark detects these signals using a system of jelly-filled pores, called ampullae of Lorenzini, on its snout. This enables them to find animals such as flatfish or crabs buried in mud. The wide head of the hammerhead shark provides more space for these pores, so these sharks have even better electroreception.

EYES

Sharks also use their eyes to find prey, especially the fast-moving sharks that hunt in the open ocean. Sharks' eyes are placed on the sides of their head, so they have good all-around vision. However, they can only see up to about 49 ft. (15m) or so in front of them, which means that sight is only important when they are closing in on their prey.

To protect their eyes when they attack prey, sharks have two eyelids, one at the top and one at the bottom of each eye, which close to cover the eye. But in requiem sharks the eyelids do not meet so they have a third eyelid, called a nictitating membrane, which covers and protects their eyes when they move in to attack. The great white shark does not have this membrane, so it protects its eyes by rolling them back into the sockets, revealing a hard pad on the back of the eye.

LATERAL LINE

Sharks can detect vibrations in the water using their lateral lines that run from head to tail down either side of their body. The lateral line is formed from water-filled tubes that lie just under the skin. A vibration In the water pushes on the lateral line and this tells the shark that there may be an animal in the water.

The ampullae of Lorenzini on the snout allow a shark to build up an electrical map of their surroundings.

BULLHEAD SHARK

With a name like bullhead, it sounds as if this shark should be large. But the bullhead is a small shark that barely reaches 5ft. (1.5m).

▼ The bullheads use their paired fins to crawl along the seabed.

▼ The mouth of the Japanese bullhead is found on the underside of its snout. There are two flaps hanging down from the nostrils to the mouth.

SHARK BITES

The teeth toward the back of the bullhead's mouth are large and flat. They are the ideal shape for grinding on the shells of their prey.

SHARK FILES

COMMON NAME: Japanese bullhead
LATIN NAME: *Heterodontus japonicus*
LENGTH: The Japanese bullhead grows to 3-4ft. (1-1.2m), the Mexican bullhead is only 27in. (70cm) long.
WEIGHT: Both are about 11-17lbs, (5-8kg)
DIET: Invertebrates, such as crabs, clams, sea urchins, and small fish
STATUS: Not listed
MUST KNOW: The female Japanese bullheads lay their eggs in nests shared by several other females.

WHERE IN THE WORLD...

The Mexican bullhead is found in the Pacific Ocean, from southern California to Ecuador. The Japanese bullhead is found in the eastern Pacific Ocean, from Japan and south to Taiwan.

Blue = Mexican bullhead Red = Japanese bullhead

SWIMS AND CRAWLS

There are a number of species of bullhead sharks, including the Japanese and Mexican bullheads. Bullhead sharks are related to the horn sharks. Bullhead sharks are slow moving. They prefer rocky seabeds but are also found in kelp forests in shallow water. The Japanese bullhead, for example, is found in water that is about 20–120 ft. (6–37m) deep. It swims and crawls over the seabed using its fins.

Bullhead sharks are nocturnal, coming out at night to hunt. During the day, they rest, hiding under rocks and in caves.

REPRODUCTION

Bullhead sharks are egg–layers. The females lay eggs in large, screw–like egg cases. There are short tendrils on the corners of each egg case, and these wrap around rocks and seaweed to prevent the egg from being carried away by the currents. The females lay two eggs at a time, and often a number of females will lay their eggs in the same place. The eggs take a long time to hatch, almost one year, and during this time there is a chance they will be eaten by other animals. The young pups are about 7 in. (18cm) long when they hatch.

APPEARANCE

Bullheads are small sharks with a stout body and blunt snout. They have a knob above each eye like a bull's horns, which is why they were named bullhead. They have two large dorsal fins, each with a spine. The Japanese bullhead has brown bands and stripes.

CARIBBEAN REEF SHARK

The Caribbean reef shark is the most common shark found in the warm waters of the Caribbean Sea. It is a type of requiem shark.

WHERE IN THE WORLD...

Caribbean reef sharks are found in the western Atlantic, from North Carolina and south to Brazil. Although they like shallow water, they are known to dive to depths of, 210ft. (370m) or more.

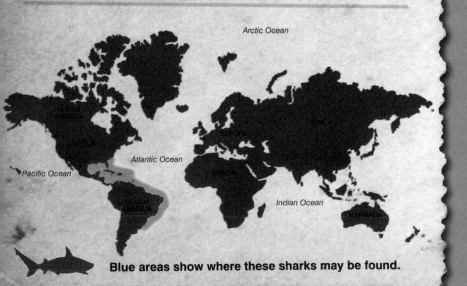

Arctic Ocean

NORTH AMERICA

ASIA

EUROPE

U.S.A.

Atlantic Ocean

AFRICA

Pacific Ocean

SOUTH AMERICA

Indian Ocean

AUSTRALIA

Blue areas show where these sharks may be found.

ON PATROL

The favorite places of this large shark to hunt are coral reefs, where they patrol the ocean where the seabed drops into the deep. Caribbean reef sharks come out at night to hunt squids and fish. These sharks have a special way of catching food. They swing their head sideways to catch their prey in the corner of their mouth. They can also pick up very low-pitch sounds, such as those made by struggling fish in the water. This helps them find prey that is easy to catch. Their upper teeth are narrow with a wide base and serrated edges that can easily tear through flesh. When threatened, the Caribbean reef shark behaves in a particular way to warn off predators and divers. It drops its pectoral fins, arches its back like a cat, and swings its head from side to side. This is to make itself look much bigger than it is.

REPRODUCTION

Although this shark is common, little is known about its reproduction. The female sharks are pregnant for about one year and they give birth to between four and six pups, each of which is about 28 in. (70cm) long. It is possible that the females swim to nursery areas to give birth. Young sharks prefer shallow water, where they are safe from predators such as bull and tiger sharks.

◀ The Caribbean reef shark tends to stay in shallow water less than 100 ft. (30m) deep.

SHARK FILES

COMMON NAME:	Caribbean reef shark
LATIN NAME:	Carcharhinus perezi
LENGTH:	Mostly 6.5-8ft. (2-2.5m), but can grow to 10ft. (3m)
WEIGHT:	Up to 154 lbs. (70 kg)
DIET:	Squids, rays, and other fish
STATUS:	Near threatened
MUST KNOW:	The females have scars over their body, and scientists think that these are caused by males who bite them during mating.

APPEARANCE

The Caribbean reef shark has a streamlined shape. It is dark gray to brown on top and white underneath and has a pale white band along its sides. Its snout is broad and rounded at the front, and its eyes are large. The first dorsal fin is large and shaped like a sickle, and its pectoral fins are long and narrow and end in a point.

▼ Reef sharks can put on a sudden burst of speed to catch fish.

SHARK BITES

During the day, these sharks lie motionless on the seabed or in caves, and for this reason they are often nicknamed the sleeping shark.

CARPET SHARK

▼ The dark band of the necklace carpet shark can be seen just behind its head.

Carpet sharks get their name from their markings, which look similar to the patterns used on some carpets. One of the most attractive is the necklace carpet shark.

NOCTURNAL SHARKS

The necklace carpet shark belongs to a small group of Australian carpet sharks that includes the collared and rusty carpet sharks. These sharks live close to sandy seabeds, rocky reefs, and in kelp beds and seagrass beds. They like shallow water but may dive to depths of more than 590 ft. (180m). They are mostly nocturnal sharks, hiding in caves and under rocks during the day and coming out at night to hunt.

Carpet sharks feed on animals that they find on the seabed, such as worms and crabs. They are small sharks, so they are eaten by larger sharks and even dolphins. Carpet sharks are harmless and can be approached by divers, but they do not like being handled. They thrash around violently if they are picked up.

WHERE IN THE WORLD...

The necklace carpet shark is found in the south Pacific Ocean along the west and south coasts of Australia, from Western Australia to Tasmania. The collared carpet shark is found along the east coast of Australia, while the rusty carpet shark is found along the south coast.

Blue areas show where these sharks may be found.

▲ The rusty carpet shark does not have the dark band behind its head. Instead, it has faint brown saddles down its body and brown spots.

REPRODUCTION

Carpet sharks lay round eggs that have two long horns. The females lay two eggs at a time, at intervals of between 12 and 39 days. Scientists are unsure how long the eggs remain on the seabed before they hatch, but it is thought to be several months.

APPEARANCE

The necklace carpet shark has a long, tube-like body, with a short, rounded snout and slit-like eyes. It is dark brown with dark and white blotches on its body and black blotches over its fins. It is called the necklace carpet shark because it has a dark band behind its head with white spots that look like a row of pearls.

The collared carpet shark has a brown to black collar behind its eyes, but there are no white spots. The rusty carpet shark does not have a dark collar, but it does have a series of broad brown bands or saddles down its body, with brown spots on its body and fins.

SHARK BITES

The egg cases of the necklace carpet shark are a favorite food of marine snails that eat their way through the case to reach the egg yolk inside.

SHARK FILES

COMMON NAME: Necklace carpet shark
LATIN NAME: *Parascyllium variolatum*
LENGTH: Mostly about 23-35 in. (60-90cm)
WEIGHT: 22 lbs. (10kg)
DIET: Invertebrates, such as crabs, shrimp, and worms
STATUS: Least concern
MUST KNOW: The necklace carpet shark is also called the varied carpet shark, ring-necked catshark, and southern catshark.

CHAIN CATSHARK

The black markings of the chain catshark may look strange, but they provide the shark with perfect camouflage for life on the rocky seabed.

ROCK BOTTOM

Chain catsharks prefer rocky seabeds to sandy ones, as the rocks provide them with shelter from predators such as tuna and other sharks. Also their black web-like markings blend in well with the rocky seabed. These catsharks are fussy about the temperature of the water, preferring temperatures of about 46-51°F (8-11°C).

▲ The egg case contains a large egg yolk that is rich in protein and fat. This nourishes the developing shark.

The chain catsharks that live in the northern parts of their range are found in shallow water, about 100-755 ft. (30-230m) deep. However, sharks living in the south are rarely found above 1,476 ft. (450m). This is because the water closer to the surface is too warm for them.

SHARK FILES

COMMON NAME: Chain catshark
LATIN NAME: Scyliorhinus retifer
LENGTH: Females 13 in. (35cm), males 15-18 in. (40-48cm)
WEIGHT: 4-11 lbs. (2-5kg)
DIET: Marine worms, squids, crustaceans, and fish
STATUS: Least concern
MUST KNOW: The rounded egg case of the chain catshark has a tendril at each corner that wraps around objects such as rocks, seaweeds, and coral to stop the egg case from being carried away by the currents.

REPRODUCTION

Catsharks are egg-laying sharks. The females start laying eggs when they are about nine years of age. The egg case is shaped like a box and is about 2 in. (5cm) long by 0.78 in. (2cm) wide. The cases are amber in color with white bands. A female catshark may lay up to 50 eggs per year. The young sharks hatch after 7 to 12 months and are about 4 in. (10cm) long.

Chain catsharks are found in the northwest and western Atlantic, along the east coast of the U.S.A., the Gulf of Mexico, and south as far as Nicaragua. They are also found in the Caribbean.

Arctic Ocean

NORTH
AMERICA

ASIA

U.S.A.

EUROPE

Atlantic Ocean

AFRICA

Pacific Ocean

Indian Ocean

AUSTRALIA

Blue areas show where these sharks may be found.

APPEARANCE

The chain catshark is a small, slender shark, reddish brown and covered in a chain-like pattern of black lines. It has a blunt snout and large, oval eyes, which are a bright emerald green. Its two dorsal fins are positioned far back along its body, and the pectoral fins are broad and short. The chain catshark has narrow, triangular teeth with smooth edges that are ideal for gripping worms and other animals.

▼ The chain-like markings make the chain catshark easy to identify.

SHARK BITES

Chain catsharks can stay motionless on the seabed, where their camouflage makes them almost impossible to see.

SHARK REPRODUCTION

Most fish lay many small eggs that they abandon in the water. There are egg-laying sharks, but there are also some sharks that give birth to live young called pups.

EGG LAYERS

About one in every three types of sharks lays eggs, for example bullhead sharks, catsharks, and dogfish. During mating, the male shark grips the female and releases sperm inside her body to fertilize the eggs. The eggs are large and protected inside a tough, rubbery egg case. Some egg cases are up to 10 in. (25cm) long. Many have tendrils at the corners that wrap around seaweed and rocks to stop the egg case from being carried away.

Inside the egg case is the unborn shark and a large yolk, which supplies it with food. When the yolk is all gone, the egg case splits open and the young shark wriggles out. The time it takes for an egg to hatch varies. Some hatch within a few weeks, but most take several months or more. Empty egg cases are often washed up onto beaches.

Egg cases, such as this one belonging to a dogfish, are also known as mermaid's purses.

The corkscrew-shaped egg cases of a Port Jackson shark.

LIVE YOUNG

Other sharks give birth to live young. After mating, the females keep the eggs inside their body, where they are protected and so are more are likely to survive. The pups emerge from their mother's body looking like miniature versions of the adult. They can be about 18-24 in. (45-60cm) long.

The hammerhead and requiem sharks have a more advanced form of reproduction. There is a link between the mother and the unborn pups, so that the mother can nourish the pups as they grow inside her. Sometimes, the female produces extra eggs that are eaten by the pups.

Not all unborn sharks are safe in their mother's body. A pup's jaws start to form within the first month. In some sharks, such as the sand tiger shark, the larger unborn pups feed on the smaller ones, so that only the biggest survive until birth.

Female sharks are pregnant from 6 to 22 months, depending on the type of shark. A female great white shark, for example, is pregnant for about 14 months and gives birth to about six to ten pups, each about 5 ft. (1.5m) long!

SHARK NURSERIES

Often female sharks swim to safe, protected areas in shallow water to give birth in a place where there are few predators and plenty of food. These are called nursery areas. The water is too shallow for the larger sharks, such as bull sharks, that prey upon young pups. The pups stay in the nursery for many months so they can feed and grow. When they are large enough, they swim into deeper water.

Sharks grow slowly, just a couple of inches per year. This means that it takes them as long as 20 years to reach full size.

Many young sharks have different markings from the adults. This tiger shark has very distinctive "spots" that fade in the adult.

COOKIE CUTTER SHARK

The cookie cutter may be small, but it has a fierce reputation. It gets its name from the shape of the round scars that it leaves in its prey after it has ripped out a mouthful of their flesh.

▼ The underside of the cookie cutter shark is covered in light-producing structures called photophores that give out a green glow. This makes it hard to see from below.

SHARK BITES

Cookie cutters are rarely seen because they live in the open ocean. Scientists have learned all they know about this shark from specimens that have been caught in nets or washed up on beaches.

▼ It is not uncommon to see seals and dolphins, such as these spinner dolphins, covered in scars from cookie cutter bites.

fleshy lips surround the mouth.

sharp-edged teeth to slice through skin.

◄ it's easy to see how the sharp teeth of this shark leave cookie-shaped scars in its victims

FIERCE BITER

The aggressive cookie cutter shark is known to bite almost any animal it finds in the ocean, including whales, dolphins, seals, other sharks, rays, and fish. It has a round mouth that is surrounded by large, fleshy lips. The upper teeth are small and narrow, while the lower teeth are larger and knife like. All the teeth have smooth edges that slice through flesh. Once it finds its prey, the cookie cutter latches onto its side, sucking with its lips to get a good grip, then it bites. The top teeth stab into the flesh, and the lower teeth slice upward, then the shark twists so that its teeth remove a perfect circle of flesh. Cookie cutters regularly replace their teeth, but instead of replacing them one by one, they replace a whole row at a time. They swallow their old teeth, as they contain nutrients that are good for the shark.

REPRODUCTION

Little is known about the reproduction of these sharks. They give birth to between 6 and 12 young. Scientists think that the females give birth in safe nursery areas close to the coastline of ocean islands.

WHERE IN THE WORLD...

Cookie cutters are found throughout the tropical regions of the Atlantic, Indian, and Pacific oceans. Sometimes, they dive as deep as 9,840 ft. (3,000m) where the water is cold and black.

Arctic Ocean

NORTH AMERICA

U.S.A.

EUROPE

ASIA

Pacific Ocean

Atlantic Ocean

AFRICA

SOUTH AMERICA

Indian Ocean

AUSTRALIA

Blue areas show where these sharks may be found.

APPEARANCE

Cookie cutter sharks have a long, cigar-shaped body. They have large green eyes, a blunt snout, and their nostrils have a flap of skin hanging down in front. They are dark brown on the back and a paler brown below. They have a dark band like a collar behind their head.

DOGFISH SHARK

Dogfish are small sharks, and one of the best known is the spiny dogfish. This dogfish has two nasty looking spines on its back to frighten off predators, but it is harmless to divers.

SHARK FILES

COMMON NAME: Spiny dogfish shark
LATIN NAME: Squalus acanthias
LENGTH: Males up to 3 ft. (1m), females up to 4.9 ft. (1.5m)
WEIGHT: Between 11-22 lbs. (5-10kg)
DIET: Squids, octopus, crustaceans, and fish, such as salmon
STATUS: Vulnerable and critically endangered in the northeast Atlantic
MUST KNOW: The spiny dogfish was once the most numerous shark in the world, but it has been overfished. It is sold as rock salmon in stores and its numbers have dropped to dangerously low levels.

▼ Dogfish got their name because they hunt in packs like dogs.

SAND AND MUD

The spiny dogfish likes shallow, warm water and lives on the seabed to depths of up to 2,952 ft. (900m). It prefers seabeds that are covered in sand and mud, rather than rock. It is also seen in estuaries. Dogfish tend to live with other spiny dogfish or even to form schools with other sharks, such as leopard and smoothhound sharks. Some schools can contain thousands of sharks.

The dogfish uses its spines for defense. If a dogfish is grabbed by a predator, it arches its back so that its spines stab the animal. This makes the predator let go of the shark, and the spines also release a poison into the flesh of the predator.

REPRODUCTION

The female spiny dogfish may be pregnant for up to two years, the longest of any vertebrate animal. She gives birth to up to 20 pups, each of which is about 8-12 in. (20-30cm) long. The young sharks grow slowly, and the females are not ready to lay eggs until they are 20 years old. The average life span of these sharks is 30 years, but a few live much longer. These sharks are incredibly slow to increase in number, so they are at risk if they are overfished.

APPEARANCE

Spiny dogfish are small sharks with a spine in front of each dorsal fin. They are a dark gray-brown on top and pale brown underneath, with white spots along the back.

WHERE IN THE WORLD...

Spiny dogfish are found in temperate waters around the world, such as the coastal waters of Europe, North America, and China. They are also found around the southern coasts of South America, Africa, and Australia. They prefer a water temperature of between 40-60 °F (6-15 °C).

Arctic Ocean

NORTH AMERICA

U.S.A.

Pacific Ocean

Atlantic Ocean

EUROPE

ASIA

AFRICA

SOUTH AMERICA

Indian Ocean

AUSTRALIA

Blue areas show where these sharks may be found.

◀ Spiny dogfish may live to 100 years, more than any other shark.

SHARK BITES

Spiny dogfish migrate over long distances. One tagged individual was recorded as swimming from the coast of British Columbia, Canada, to Japan, a distance of 4,350 mi. (7,000km).

DUSKY SHARK

▼ The dusky shark has a particularly rounded snout.

This shark gets its name from the dusky-colored tips seen on the fins of young sharks. A member of the requiem shark family, the dusky shark is a top predator in tropical oceans.

WHERE IN THE WORLD...

The dusky shark is found across the subtropical seas and oceans of the world, such as the Red Sea and Caribbean, Indian, and Pacific oceans. It prefers coastal and shallow water.

Arctic Ocean

Atlantic Ocean

Pacific Ocean

Indian Ocean

WARM WATER

The dusky shark is known to swim long distances, which is why it is found all around the world. For example, dusky sharks living in the western Atlantic and eastern Pacific oceans make regular migrations. They swim north in the summer and then south in the winter to where there is warmer water. Interestingly, the males and females make these journeys separately in schools consisting of all males or all females.

The dusky shark hunts close to the seabed at depths of about 660–1,310 ft. (200–400m), but it is seen in shallow water, too.

The dusky shark is an expert hunter, feeding on a variety of animals. Young dusky sharks hunt in groups, preying on small fish such as anchovy and sardines. As they grow older and larger, dusky sharks are able to feed on large prey, such as groupers, barracudas and other big fish, dolphins, and even other sharks.

Adult dusky sharks are not preyed upon by other animals, but bull sharks hunt the youngsters.

REPRODUCTION

The female sharks give birth to between six and ten pups in shallow nursery areas, where the pups are safe from large predators such as other sharks. The females only mate and produce young every two years, and the sharks are not ready to breed until they are about 20 years of age. This means that dusky sharks are incredibly slow to increase in number and so extinction could be a problem. Dusky sharks live for about 45 years.

APPEARANCE

The dusky shark is slender and streamlined, with a rounded snout. Its upper body is blue-gray in color while the underside is white. The teeth on its upper jaw are large and triangular with serrated edges.

▼ Its slim body allows the dusky shark to slip effortlessly through the water.

SHARK FILES

COMMON NAME:	Dusky shark
LATIN NAME:	Carcharhinus obscurus
LENGTH:	Mostly 8-10 ft. (2.5-3m) but can grow to 13 ft. (4.2m)
WEIGHT:	Mostly about 350-400 lbs. (160-180kg), but some reach 750 lbs. (340kg)
DIET:	Skates, rays, squids, octopus, mollusks, crustaceans, and even dead animal bodies floating in the water.
STATUS:	Vulnerable
MUST KNOW:	So many have been killed that now the number of dusky sharks is just one-fifth of the number found in the 1970s.

SHARK BITES

Sadly, this shark is caught for meat and for shark-fin soup, and its skin is used for leather.

EPAULETTE SHARK

▼ At night, the epaulette shark crawls over the coral reef in search of small animals.

An epaulette is the name given to a decorative shoulder strap on a uniform. The epaulette shark is given this name because of the dark eyespots on both sides of its body, just behind its head.

WALKING AND CRAWLING

The epaulette shark is a type of long-tailed carpet shark. It has an odd form of movement as it almost "walks" across the seabed or coral reef where it lives. It uses the pair of sturdy fins under its body to push itself forward, while swinging its body from side to side. It also uses its broad pectoral fins to crawl in and out of rock pools on the shore.

The epaulette sharks body, is covered in brown spots and bands. These provide excellent camouflage when the shark is resting on the reef during the day. It also has two big eyespots. Scientists are not sure of the role of these eyespots. Some believe that they distract predators, while others think that they scare them away.

WHERE IN THE WORLD...
This shark lives in tropical waters, from New Guinea to northern Australia. It is found in shallow water to depths of 160 ft. (50m). It can be found in rock pools and shallow coral reefs, especially where there is staghorn coral.

Arctic Ocean

NORTH
AMERICA

EUROPE

ASIA

U.S.A.

Pacific Ocean

Atlantic Ocean

AFRICA

SOUTH
AMERICA

Indian Ocean

AUSTRALIA

Blue areas show where these sharks may be found.

▶ The epaulette shark has a large black eyespot ringed in white behind each pectoral fin.

REPRODUCTION

Female epaulette sharks are ready to breed when they are about seven years of age. The female lays two eggs at a time every two weeks, producing a total of about 50 eggs each year. The egg is oval in shape and is about 4 in. (10cm) long by 1.5 in. (4cm) wide. The eggs take about four months to hatch. Newly hatched pups are about 6 in. (15cm) long. They grow very slowly, gaining just an inch or two in length each year.

APPEARANCE

The epaulette shark has a slender, elongated body with a rounded snout. It has oval eyes, small teeth, and a pair of tiny barbels attached to its nostrils. Its pectoral fins are broad and rounded in shape. Its body is pale brown to brown with brown spots and bands.

SHARK BITES

The epaulette shark can survive many hours out of water, sheltering under rocks and in shallow rock pools until the tide returns.

SHARK FILES

COMMON NAME: Epaulette shark
LATIN NAME: Hemiscyllium ocellatum.
LENGTH: From 280-35 in. (70-90cm), a few grow to more than 3 ft. (1m).
WEIGHT: Between 11-22 lbs. (5-10kg)
DIET: Marine worms, crabs and small fish
STATUS: Least concern
MUST KNOW: This shark can survive with little oxygen by switching off some of its brain functions.

GALAPAGOS SHARK

The Galapagos shark is a large requiem shark that is common in shallow water around tropical islands. It is also called the gray reef whaler.

TERRITORY

Galapagos sharks like clear water closer to coral reefs and rocky seabeds, where they are seen in small schools. They often patrol the steep coral cliffs on the seaward side of a reef, where the cliff plunges to depths of 590 ft. (180m) or more.

This shark is aggressive and when threatened it hunches its back, drops its pectoral fins, and swings its head from side to side – a clear message that it is about to attack. It is not scared of attacking large prey animals, such as rays, fur seals, and sea lions. But most of the time, Galapagos sharks eat fish and squid they find close to the seabed.

SHARK BITES

The Galapagos shark feeds on marine iguanas, a type of reptile found only in the Galapagos Islands. The iguanas plunge into the water to get cool and become prey for the sharks.

APPEARANCE

This is a slender, streamlined shark with a wide, rounded snout and round eyes. It has large, pointed pectoral fins and a tall front dorsal fin with an angled tip. It is dark gray-brown on the top and white on the underside. The Galapagos shark is often confused with other reef sharks, especially the dusky shark and gray reef shark, so the key feature to look for is its tall dorsal fin with an angled tip.

SHARK FILES

COMMON NAME:	Galapagos shark
LATIN NAME:	Carcharhinus galapagensis
LENGTH:	Up to 9.8 ft. (3m) but the largest was 12 ft. (3.7m)
WEIGHT:	Up to 190 lbs. (85kg)
DIET:	Fish, squid,s octopus, rays, other sharks, and seals
STATUS:	Near threatened
MUST KNOW:	This is a dangerous shark. It is very inquisitive and may circle divers and even charge them.

REPRODUCTION

The female Galapagos shark is pregnant for about one year. She swims into shallow water to give birth to a litter of up to 16 babies, or pups. Each pup is about 23-31 in. (60-80cm) long. Galapagos sharks have been known to eat their young, so pups stay in the shallow water where they are safe from their parents and other predators. The females are ready to breed when they are about ten years old, and they have pups every two to three years. Galapagos sharks live for about 25 years.

▼ Galapagos sharks hunt in groups, looking for prey such as fish and iguanas. The dark "spots" around the shark's eye are small fish called remora, or sharksuckers, that like to cling on to the shark's skin.

WHERE IN THE WORLD...

The Galapagos shark is found around the Galapagos Islands, off the coast of Ecuador in South America, in the shallow waters along the coasts of Mexico and South America, as well as islands of the Pacific, Indian, and Atlantic oceans.

Arctic Ocean

NORTH AMERICA

U.S.A.

EUROPE

ASIA

Pacific Ocean

Atlantic Ocean

AFRICA

Indian Ocean

SOUTH AMERICA

AUSTRALIA

Blue areas show where these sharks may be found.

SHARKS OF THE PAST

Sharks have been around for hundreds of millions of years. The oldest known shark, called Doliodus, lived more than 400 million years ago. The fossil was found in Canada and was just 9 in. (23cm) long. Scientists think that this was a young shark. The adults would have been about 20 in. (50cm) long and looked similar to an angel shark.

This is the fossil of a shark called Pseudorhina, which may have looked similar to an angel shark.

HELICOPRION

There were some strange sharks swimming around in the ancient seas. One shark called Helicoprion lived 345 million years ago, and its fossilized teeth have been found in rocks. The teeth on its lower jaw were arranged in a spiral. For a long time, scientists have been trying to figure out how these teeth fitted into its mouth. They think that the spiral of up to 180 teeth was placed vertically on the lower jaw in a similar way to a circular saw. A close relative of Helicoprion, called Edestus, had teeth that grew beyond the tip of its snout. It would have looked like it had a pair of jagged shears attached to the front of its mouth.

STETHACANTHUS

Another strange looking shark from more than 300 million years ago was Stethacanthus. These small sharks, about 23 in. (60cm) long, had streamlined bodies. But the male had a huge, flat-topped dorsal fin covered in scales, which looked like a brush. It also had a smaller "brush" on top of its head. Scientists think that the role of these "brushes" was to make the males more attractive to the females.

MEGALODON

The largest of all the extinct sharks was Megalodon, or "big tooth". It first appeared around 15 million years ago and disappeared around 1.6 million years ago. It was a true giant of the oceans, reaching 52 ft. (16m) long and weighing about 47 tons (50 tonnes). It was the biggest fish to have lived and the second-largest predator to inhabitat the ocean (the largest is the sperm whale). The closest living relative to Megalodon

A reconstruction of a Helicoprion shark with its spiral of teeth on its lower jaw.

A tooth of the Megalodon is the size of a man's hand. The teeth sat in jaws just under 6.5 ft. (2m) across.

is the great white shark. Megalodon had a huge appetite to match its huge size, so it hunted the largest animals in the ocean at that time – whales. However, scientists think that Megalodon killed its prey in a different way from the great white shark. They believe that Megalodon grabbed the whales in its huge mouth and crushed their rib cage.

Everything we know about Megalodon comes from its teeth, as there are few other fossilized remains of this giant shark. Scientists compare the size and shape of the teeth with those of the great white and from this they can figure out the size and mass of the animal, the shape of the jaw, and even the way that the animal killed its prey.

GOBLIN SHARK

The goblin shark is probably the weirdest shark alive today. It is rarely seen because it lives in the deep ocean. The shark gets its name from the long-nosed Tengu, a dog-like creature from Japanese folklore.

SHARK BITES

The goblin shark has a gray white skin but its blood vessels run so close to the surface that they make tits skin look pink.

 ▼ The fang-shaped teeth of the goblin shark are incredibly sharp. The shark's jaws are tucked away while it swims. It extends its jaws to catch prey.

◄ The goblin shark's long snout helps it find food in the gloomy depths of the ocean.

MYSTERIOUS CREATURE

Scientists call the goblin shark a living fossil because its appearance has remained unchanged for millions of years. However, they know very little about this strange-looking shark because all of its closest relatives are now extinct and so few have been studied. Only about 50 goblin sharks have been caught, and even fewer have been seen in the wild. Scientists do not know how many are living in the oceans; most have been found around Japan.

Scientists do know that the goblin shark lives in the ocean's twilight zone. This is at a depth of below 656 ft. (200m), where there is just a glimmer of light. The goblin shark is found as deep as 4,265 ft. (1,300m) close to the seabed. Sight is of little use in the deep ocean, so the goblin shark hunts using smell and electroreception, the ability to pick up electrical charges from other animals. It does this by using the ampullae of Lorenzini on its long snout, which help it detect animals such as crabs hiding in the mud.

APPEARANCE

The goblin shark has pinkish white skin and a strange-shaped head with a long, flat, pointed snout. It has rounded pectoral fins and a small, hooked dorsal fin. The tail has one arrow-shaped lobe.
As much as a quarter of its weight is its liver. This helps keep the shark buoyant in the water and stops it from sinking.

WHERE IN THE WORLD...

Goblin sharks are found in the waters around Japan and off the coast of Africa, southern Australia, and New Zealand. They are also seen in the Atlantic, near Madeira off the coast of Portugal, and in the Gulf of Mexico.

Blue areas show where sharks may be found.

REPRODUCTION

Scientists do not know much about the shark's reproduction because no one has caught a pregnant goblin shark. However, they know that its closest living relative, the mackerel shark, gives birth to live young, so it is likely that the goblin shark does the same. But no one knows how long the female is pregnant, how many young she produces, or the size of the pups.

GREAT WHITE SHARK

The great white shark is probably the most feared animal in the ocean. It is an expert hunter with a large mouth filled with jagged teeth.

▼ The life span of the great white is between 40 and 60 years, but some may live much longer.

SHARK FILES

COMMON NAME:	Great white shark
LATIN NAME:	Carcharodon carcharias
LENGTH:	Usually about 15 ft. (4.6m) but up to 19 ft. (6m)
WEIGHT:	Up to 1,984 lbs. (900kg) but may reach 3,968 lbs. (1800kg)
DIET:	Seals and sea lions, small whales, turtles and dead animals in the water
STATUS:	Vulnerable
MUST KNOW:	Can detect one drop of blood in 22 gal. (100l.) of water and can sense tiny amounts of blood in the water up to 3 mi. (5km) away.

HUNTING TECHNIQUES

The great white shark is the world's largest predatory fish. Its size means that it is not usually hunted by any other animal in the water, so it is a top predator. However, there have been a few reports of killer whales attacking great white sharks.

Great whites hunt many different animals. They lie in ambush in the water, attacking from below. Often they hunt early in the day when the light is low so that their prey cannot see them lurking in the water. Their favorite food is a plump seal. When the shark spots a seal close to the surface, it charges at full speed, ramming into the seal's side and stunning it. Sometimes, the speed of the shark carries them out of the water. Before the seal knows what has happened, the shark takes a bite out of its side and leaves it to bleed to death in the water. Once it is dead, the shark rips it into pieces and swallows it.

Scientists are not sure how many great white sharks live in the oceans, but they do know that their numbers are declining. This is because the sharks are overfished, get caught in nets, or are killed because people fear them.

REPRODUCTION

The females are pregnant for just under one year. They can give birth to as many as 14 pups.

APPEARANCE

These sharks have a dark gray upper body, but they get their name from their white underside. Their body is streamlined with a powerful tail.

WHERE IN THE WORLD...

Great whites are found in temperate waters where the water temperature is 50–75°F (12–25°C). They are usually found down in the open ocean to depths of 4,000 ft. (1,230m) but they hunt close to shores, too.

Arctic Ocean

NORTH AMERICA

U.S.A.

EUROPE

ASIA

Atlantic Ocean

Pacific Ocean

AFRICA

SOUTH AMERICA

Indian Ocean

AUSTRALIA

Blue areas show where these sharks may be found.

◄ The jagged edges of the great white's teeth are razor-sharp and slice through flesh very easily.

SHARK BITES

Great whites do not always bite to kill. If they are not sure about an animal, they take a bite as a sample and only kill the prey if it tastes good.

GREENLAND SHARK

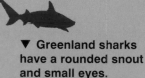

▼ Greenland sharks have a rounded snout and small eyes.

The Greenland shark lives farther north than any other shark. Its home is the icy cold water around Greenland and Iceland. It is also called the sleeper shark because it moves very slowly and spends a lot of time resting.

SLOW AND COLD

These sharks can survive in freezing water temperatures – from 30-42°F (-2-7°C) – that would kill other sharks. They survive because they have a thick layer of fat under their skin and because they lead "slow" lives, which means that they do not have to eat so much. They grow slowly, too. The adults gain about 4 in. (10cm) in length per year, less than other sharks.

SCAVENGING FOOD

The Greenland shark is a scavenger and eats food that is already dead or killed. As well

WHERE IN THE WORLD...

Greenland sharks are found around Greenland, Iceland, the northeastern coast of Canada, and the northern coast of Europe. They are found down to depths of 6, 561 ft. (2,000m). In the winter, the shark moves to shallow coastal waters and is even seen in the estuary of the St. Lawrence River in Canada.

REPRODUCTION

The female Greenland shark gives birth to live young. There are up to ten pups in a litter, each one about 15 in. (40cm) long. Many females have scars on their body that were made by the male shark biting them during mating. Fortunately, female sharks have a thick layer of blubber under their skin, so the bites to do not injure them.

APPEARANCE

Greenland sharks are slate gray to black in color with a hint of purple. Their two dorsal fins are both small. The teeth on their upper jaw are narrow and pointed, with smooth edges, while the teeth on their lower jaw are larger.

▼ A Greenland shark swims slowly through the murky water around Greenland.

SHARK FILES

COMMON NAME: Greenland shark
LATIN NAME: Somniosus microcephalus
LENGTH: 13-19 ft. (4-6m), at the largest 21 ft. (6.4m)
WEIGHT: Up to 2,200 lbs. (1,000kg)
DIET: Fish, seals, squids, and the remains of dead animals, such as polar bears
STATUS: Near threatened
MUST KNOW: Most Greenland sharks have a small parasite living on their eye called a copepod. It latches onto the outside of the eye and starts feeding on it, causing the shark to become partially blind.

SHARK BITES

No animal eats the body of a Greenland shark, even when it is dead, because the flesh is poisonous. However, many Arctic people eat the meat. The meat has to be boiled several times before it is safe to eat. The poison makes people feel very drunk.

GRAY REEF SHARK

The gray reef shark is one of the most common sharks in the Indian and Pacific oceans. It is a type of requiem shark and is most closely related to the silvertip shark. It is also called the blacktip reef shark, bronze whaler, or the shortnose blacktail shark.

▲ A large school of gray reef sharks in the clear, blue water of the Pacific Ocean.

WHERE IN THE WORLD...

These sharks are found in shallow water close to coral reefs and lagoons in the Indian and Pacific oceans. They prefer water to depths of about 200 ft. (60m), but some have been found as deep as 3,280 ft. (1,000m).

Arctic Ocean

NORTH AMERICA

U.S.A.

EUROPE

ASIA

Atlantic Ocean

AFRICA

Pacific Ocean

SOUTH AMERICA

Indian Ocean

AUSTRALIA

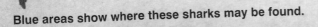

Blue areas show where these sharks may be found.

SCHOOL PATROL

Gray reef sharks are agile, fast-swimming predators. During the day, they group together to form large schools of up to 100. These schools patrol the edge of the seaward side of the reef, looking for fish and other animals to hunt. Sometimes, they swim into narrow channels in the reef where the water flows quickly. They wait for prey to swim down the channel, from where there is no escape. At night, the school separates, and the sharks hunt alone. Often they swim into shallow lagoons, where they hunt under the cover of darkness.

REPRODUCTION

The female sharks are pregnant for about one year, and they give birth to up to six pups. Each pup is about 17-23 in. (45-60cm) long. The females are ready to breed when they are about seven years old. These sharks have a life span of about 25 years.

▶ Gray reef sharks like to hunt on the seaward side of coral reefs, where the water is much deeper.

The gray reef shark is a species under threat. Its numbers are falling because it lives in shallow water and is easy to fish. The females do not produce many pups, so it will take time for their numbers to increase again. However, in the Caribbean, gray reef sharks get good protection because they are popular with tourists, especially tourists who like to dive with the sharks.

SHARK FILES

COMMON NAME: Gray reef shark
LATIN NAME: Carcharhinus amblyrhynchos
LENGTH: About 5-6.5 ft. (1.5-2m)
WEIGHT: 55-75 lbs. (25-34kg)
DIET: Fish, such as eel, grouper, and triggerfish, as well as squids, crab, and shrimp
STATUS: Near threatened
MUST KNOW: Gray reef sharks are very curious animals, and they swim up to divers. But they do not like being touched or cornered.

SHARK BITES

Schools of gray reef sharks have been seen to herd smaller fish against a reef face, where they cannot escape, and then the sharks attack together.

APPEARANCE

Grey reef sharks are dark gray to bronze gray on their upper side and white on their underside. They have a white tip to their dorsal fin and black tips on their other fins. Their tail fin has a black edge. Their snout is broad with a rounded tip, and their eyes are large.

HAMMERHEAD SHARK

The hammerhead is instantly recognizable with its hammer-shaped head. There are nine species of hammerheads, one of the most common is the scalloped hammerhead.

BETTER SENSES

Scientists are not sure why these sharks have their hammer-shaped head. Some scientists think that it acts like a stabilizer enabling the shark to turn sharply without rolling in the water. But the more likely reason is that it provides better senses. The shark's eyes are at the ends of the hammer, and this gives it all round vision. There is more space for the ampullae of Lorenzini, so hammerheads have excellent electroreception, and their nostrils are farther apart so they can "taste" more water, which helps them track down prey.

SHARK FILES

COMMON NAME: Scalloped hammerhead
LATIN NAME: Sphyrna lewini
LENGTH: Females reach 13 ft. (4m) but males are smaller
WEIGHT: 440-550 lbs. (200-250kg)
DIET: Sardines, herring, squids, crabs, rays, and small sharks, such as sharpnose and blacktip reef sharks
STATUS: Endangered
MUST KNOW: All hammerhead species are at risk from extinction. The main reason is that they are hunted just for their fins, but they also become trapped in nets meant for other species.

REPRODUCTION

At certain times of the year, huge schools of hundreds of hammerheads are seen in certain parts of the ocean called breeding grounds. The females gather in the middle of the school with the largest females right in the center. The largest females are the oldest, and they are the most desirable. Most female hammerheads have scars on their bodies caused by the males gripping them with their teeth during mating.

The females are pregnant for about ten months, and they give birth to up to 30 pups. The pups are about 20 in. (50cm) long and have soft hammers so that the female is not injured when the pup is born. The hammerhead pups stay in shallow water while they are young and only move into deeper water when they are larger and safe from predators.

APPEARANCE

The hammer of the scalloped hammerhead has a notched front edge. The shark is light brown to olive or bronze in color, with a white underside. It has a very tall dorsal fin.

WHERE IN THE WORLD...

Scalloped hammerheads are found in tropical and temperate waters. They live in shallow coastal water as well as deep water up to 900 ft. (275m) down or deeper. They are found around islands such as the Maldives, where the seabed slopes steeply into deep water.

Arctic Ocean

NORTH
AMERICA

U.S.A.

EUROPE

ASIA

Pacific Ocean

Atlantic Ocean

AFRICA

SOUTH
AMERICA

Indian Ocean

AUSTRALIA

Blue areas show where these sharks may be found.

SHARK BITES

Hammerheads use their hammers to attack stingrays – they pin the animal to the seabed with their hammer and bite its wings.

dorsal fin

hammer-shaped head

eye

scalloped edge

HOUNDSHARK

There are more than 40 different types of houndsharks, and they are divided into groups, according to how closely related they are. One group with the Latin name *Triakis* contains five types of houndsharks. They are the banded, sharpfin, spotted, sharptooth houndshark, and leopard shark.

▼ Houndsharks have a distinctive wrinkle near their mouth and a flap of skin hanging from their nostrils.

▲ The houndshark's long, blade - like teeth are very sharp and grip fish easily.

WHERE IN THE WORLD...

Banded houndsharks are found in the shallow coastal water of the northwest Pacific ocean, from Siberia to Taiwan and Japan. The spotted houndshark is found in the eastern Pacific Ocean, along the coast of South America, from Peru to Chile and the Galapagos Islands. The sharptooth houndshark is found along the coast of Namibia and South Africa.

Yellow = spotted houndshark, Red = sharptooth houndshark, Blue = banded houndshark

BANDED AND SHARPFIN HOUNDSHARKS

The banded houndshark lives on the seabed in shallow water close to the shore. It likes estuaries and shallow bays, where there is a sandy seabed with lots of eelgrass and seaweed. Most of the time it lives on its own, but small groups have been seen resting together during the day.

The sharpfin houndshark is only found off the coast of Ecuador. Scientists know very little about this shark, as only two specimens have ever been found, and they were caught in fishing nets. No one has been able to study these sharks in the wild.

APPEARANCE

The banded houndshark has a long, cylindrical body, with a rounded snout and oval eyes. The mouth is on the underside of its snout. It has wrinkles running back from the corner of its mouth and a flap of skin hanging down from the top of each nostril. It has two large, spineless dorsal fins. Running down the back of the young sharks are ten saddle-like black marks and several small blackish brown dots.

REPRODUCTION

The females give birth to live pups. The banded houndshark has litters of up to 20 pups, but the sharpfin may produce as many as 26 pups. Each pup is about 11-15 in. (30-40cm) in length.

SHARK BITES

The bands and spots of the young sharks fade with age, and some adults do not have any bands or spots at all.

LEMON SHARK

This shark gets its name from its pale yellowish brown color. It is a timid shark that swims away from divers.

WHERE IN THE WORLD...

Lemon sharks are found along the coasts of North and South America, in the Caribbean, and in the Gulf of Mexico. They are also found along the west coast of Africa.

Arctic Ocean

Atlantic Ocean

Pacific Ocean

Indian Ocean

Blue areas show where these sharks may be found.

MIGRATION

Lemon sharks like warm, shallow water, and they are rarely found deeper than 330 ft. (100m). They live in a variety of habitats, including coral reefs, mangrove swamps, bays, and river estuaries. Every year, they migrate along the coast, moving further away from the equator during the warm summer months and returning to tropical areas for the winter.

Lemon sharks form schools of up to 30 individuals, which are of the same sex and age. They are active during the day and night. They gather in shallow water during the night but move into deeper water during the day.

These sharks are under threat because they are fished for their fins. Also, habitats such as mangrove swamps, which are important to the survival of the young sharks, are being cleared.

APPEARANCE

Lemon sharks have a yellowish brown body, a broad, rounded snout, and large eyes. The second dorsal fin is almost as large as the first one.

▼ Groups of lemon sharks are often seen in shallow water near docks and piers.

SHARK FILES

COMMON NAME: Lemon shark
LATIN NAME: Negaprion brevirostris
LENGTH: 2-3 m (6.5–10ft) but longest recorded was about 3.6 m (12ft)
WEIGHT: Largest recorded was 184 kg (405lbs)
DIET: Fish such as catfish, mullet, cowfish and stingrays, and guitarfish, crabs, seabirds and, even small sharks
STATUS: Near threatened
MUST KNOW: Lemon sharks can live in fresh water so they are sometimes found in rivers.

REPRODUCTION

The sharks mate in shallow water during the spring, and the females are pregnant for as long as one year. They return to shallow waters again to give birth to up to 17 pups, each of which is about 19-28 in. (50-70cm) in length. The young sharks grow very slowly, only putting on 4-6 in. (10-15cm) of growth in their first year. For this reason, they remain in the safety of shallow water for several years before venturing out to sea. The young sharks are often found in mangrove swamps, where they feed on fish and invertebrate animals, such as crabs. Lemon sharks are ready to breed by the time they are 10 to 15 years old. Their life span is about 25 years.

▼ Lemon sharks can be dangerous if threatened. If they lose, break, or wear down a tooth, it is replaced by a new one, which rotates into place.

LEOPARD SHARK

▼ Leopard sharks like to hunt close to the seabed, where they feed on worms and crustaceans.

The leopard shark is a type of houndshark. It gets its name from the black marks over its body that looks similar to leopard spots.

NIGHT HUNTERS

The favorite habitats of the leopard shark are bays and estuaries, where the seabed is covered by sand and mud. They are also seen in kelp beds and reefs close to the coast. Leopard sharks are more active at night. Often, groups of leopard sharks are seen following the tide to hunt animals on mudflats and in other shallow areas. Sometimes, they swim into such shallow water that they get stranded when the tide goes out.

Leopard sharks eat a varied diet, hunting clams, crabs, shrimp and fish. Leopard sharks also love to eat worms, but they are very difficult to catch. The sharks shape their lips into a tube so they can suck the worms out of their burrow. Then they grip them with their sharp teeth.

Usually leopard sharks stay in the same area all their lives, but sharks in more northern regions may swim south in the winter and return when the water warms up in the spring.

WHERE IN THE WORLD. . .

Leopard sharks are found in the temperate waters of the northeastern Pacific ocean, from Oregon to Mexico. Most are found in shallow water of less than 30 ft. (10m) in depth, but they have been seen in deeper water of up to 330 ft. (100m).

Arctic Ocean

NORTH AMERICA

U.S.A

EUROPE

ASIA

Pacific Ocean

Atlantic Ocean

AFRICA

SOUTH AMERICA

Indian Ocean

AUSTRALIA

Blue areas show where these sharks may be found.

▲ Leopard sharks sometimes hunt in cloudy water in or close to kelp beds.

SHARK BITES

Most leopard sharks live in a home range or territory where they hunt and sleep. They rarely travel out of this area.

APPEARANCE

Leopard sharks have a long body, with a short, rounded snout. Their large eyes are oval in shape, with a third eyelid. They have a silver-gray body with large, black spots and saddle-shaped marks. The underside is pale gray to white. The two dorsal fins are large, and the pectoral fins have a triangular shape.

REPRODUCTION

Leopard sharks give birth to live young. They can have up to 30 or more young in a litter, and the average size of a pup is about 8 in. (20cm) long. Leopard sharks are ready to breed when they are about ten years old. They live for about 30 years.

Leopard sharks live together in large schools. The sharks within one schools are of the same sex and age.

SHARK FILES

COMMON NAME: Leopard shark
LATIN NAME: Triakis semifasciata
LENGTH: 4-5 ft. (1.2-1.5m)
WEIGHT: About 2-26 lbs. (1-12kg) the largest grow to 40 lbs. (18kg)
DIET: Animals on the seabed, such as crabs, shrimp, fish, worms, and even young rays and other small sharks
STATUS: Least concern
MUST KNOW: During the day, leopard sharks rest on the seabed.

73

MAKO SHARK

Mako sharks are the sprinters of the shark world, swimming at amazing speeds of up to 20 mph. (32km/h). They can even leap out of the water. There are two types of mako sharks, the shortfin and the rare longfin.

FAST MOVERS

The shortfin mako shark has a streamlined shape that allows it to slip easily through the water. This shark can keep its muscles at a higher temperature than the surrounding water so it is more active. This means that it can swim fast enough to catch fish such as tuna and swordfish, which are usually too quick for other predators.

▼ The mako shark has a mouth full of sharp, dagger-like teeth for catching fish.

Mako sharks ambush their prey. They dive deep into the water and wait for their prey to appear above them. Then they charge straight up unnoticed from below, and take a bite out of their prey. Mako sharks eat a lot of food, as they need energy to keep their body warm.

Mako shark numbers are falling. They are popular game fish and are caught in large quantities by deep-sea fishermen. They are also very slow to reproduce, as the females only have young every three years or so. This means that it takes a long time for the numbers of mako sharks to increase.

SHARK FILES

COMMON NAME: Shortfin mako shark
LATIN NAME: Isurus oxyrinchus
LENGTH: Up to 10.4 ft. (3.2m)
WEIGHT: About 880 lbs. (400kg) with the heaviest reaching 1,000b lbs. (450kg)
DIET: Squids, tuna, mackerel, swordfish, other sharks, porpoise, and sea turtles
STATUS: Vulnerable
MUST KNOW: Some scientists estimate that makos have to eat 3 percent of their body weight in food every day; that's about 26 lbs. (12kg)

REPRODUCTION

The females are pregnant for at least one year, and in some cases for as long as 18 months. During this time, the unborn pups feed on unfertilized eggs inside the female's body.

APPEARANCE

WHERE IN THE WORLD...

Worldwide in open ocean, tropical and temperate waters, and in deep tropical water down to 490 ft. (150m), never in water colder than 60°F (16°C).

Arctic Ocean

NORTH AMERICA

U.S.A

EUROPE

ASIA

Pacific Ocean

Atlantic Ocean

AFRICA

Indian Ocean

SOUTH AMERICA

AUSTRALIA

Blue areas show where these sharks may be found.

SHARK BITES

Mako sharks have been known to jump into fishing boats and injure fishermen.

MEGAMOUTH SHARK

The megamouth was only discovered in 1976, when one was caught in a net. Since then fewer than 50 megamouths have been caught or observed in the wild. Very little is known about this deep-water shark with the huge mouth.

SHARK BITES

Scientists did not think that megamouths had any predators, so a group of divers watching some sperm whales were amazed to see them attack a megamouth.

▼ There are rows of tiny teeth inside those large lips.

BIG MOUTH, SMALL FOOD

The megamouth is a filter feeder, like the basking shark that is its closest relative. It feeds on plankton, krill, and small fish. Scientists are not sure how the megamouth feeds. Scientists think that it swims through the water with its mouth open, like the basking shark.

Planktonic animals (animals that feed on plankton) spend the night close to the surface of the water where they can feed under the cover of darkness. At dawn, they sink to the depths, where they spend the day, only returning to the surface again at dusk. Megamouths have been seen to do the same, so they are probably following the plankton. One shark was caught and tagged so that its movements could be recorded. It spent the night at a depth of 50 ft. (15m) and during the day it was at depths of about 490 ft. (150m).

Many animals that live in the deep have ways of producing their own light, including the megamouth. Its mouth is edged with small round structures called photophores. These are light-producing organs that give out an eerie green light. The light attracts plankton and krill that are then eaten by the shark.

SHARK FILES

COMMON NAME:	Megamouth
LATIN NAME:	Megachasma pelagios
LENGTH:	Up to 18 ft. (5.5m)
WEIGHT:	2,200-2,645 lbs. (1,000-1,200kg)
DIET:	Plankton, small fish
STATUS:	Not listed
MUST KNOW:	Most megamouths have scars from the teeth of the cookie cutter shark.

WHERE IN THE WORLD...
Megamouths are found in the tropical waters of the Atlantic, Indian, and Pacific oceans to depths of about 3,280 ft. (1,000m).

Arctic Ocean

NORTH AMERICA

U.S.A.

EUROPE

ASIA

Pacific Ocean

Atlantic Ocean

AFRICA

SOUTH AMERICA

Indian Ocean

AUSTRALIA

Blue areas show where these sharks may be found

REPRODUCTION

Little is known about the reproduction of the megamouth because so few females have been caught and examined. They give birth to live young, like their close relatives the mackerel sharks. However, it is unknown for how long the females are pregnant and how many young they produce.

APPEARANCE

The megamouth has a large mouth with rubbery lips. Inside there are up to 50 rows of very small, hooked teeth. Its flabby body is a black-brown color on the upperside and almost white on the underside. It has two dorsal fins, with the front one twice the size of the back one. Its tail fin has one lobe much larger than the other.

SHARK ATTACK

Sharks are the most feared animals in the ocean, but shark attacks on people are rare and very few people die as a result of being attacked by a shark.

A warning bell is rung if a shark is spotted in the water near this beach.

HOW MANY ATTACKS?

Each year, there are between 50 and 70 shark attacks around the world and fewer than 15 people die from their injuries. In the United States, there are about 15 attacks per year, and one person dies every two years. For example, in 2010 a kite surfer was killed just 1,640 ft (500m) from the shore in Florida. Unusually, he was surrounded by a group of sharks that bit him many times.

There has been a steady increase in attacks over the last 20 years because more people are involved in water activities, such as swimming, surfboarding, and diving.

THE TOP FOUR

Only four species of sharks are responsible for the majority of shark attacks. They are the great white, oceanic whitetip, tiger, and bull sharks. However, many more may attack if they are provoked or made nervous by divers.

PROTECTED BEACHES

Swimmers and surfers can be protected from shark attacks by placing a shark net under the water around a beach. The net is placed about 13 ft (4m) under the water so that boats can leave the beach, but sharks can't get in, although some types of sharks may be able to slip over the top of the net. The mesh size is large enough to trap sharks, but too large to catch fish. However, these nets may also catch turtles and dolphins. There are 51 beaches along the coast of New South Wales in Australia that are protected by shark nets, and there has been only one reported attack in the 70 years since the nets were installed.

Another way to protect a beach is to use a drum line. This is a long line with hooks weighed down by old oil drums. The line is positioned around the beach, and then the hooks are baited to catch sharks. However, these lines often result in the deaths of the sharks, which is a huge disadvantage, as shark numbers are falling rapidly.

Far fewer people are
killed by sharks, such
as this great white,
than are killed
by tigers.

HOW TO SURVIVE
A SHARK ATTACK

So what do you do if you find yourself in the water
with a great white shark? Get out of the water as
quickly as possible, but stay calm, as thrashing
around in the water will only attract the shark. If you
have a cut or a graze that is bleeding, you should
get out of the water immediately, as the blood will
attract any shark nearby. Don't wear jewelry in
the water – sparkling and glittering silver can look
like fish scales and attract a shark.

A shark took a large bite out of
this surfboard.

Watch the shark at all times. It may disappear, but
sharks often swim away and then come back. If
you are stuck in the water, try and find something
to back up against, such as a large rock or a reef.
That way the shark cannot sneak up behind you.

If a shark attacks, hit it hard in the eyes or gill slits
but not the nose. Use your fists, feet, elbows, or
an object such as a rock or even a camera. If you
know there are sharks in the area, do not get in
the water in the first place.

NURSE SHARK

The nurse shark is one of the many reef sharks that is found in shallow water. It is a slow-moving shark that is not usually dangerous unless it feels threatened by divers.

SHARK FILES

COMMON NAME: Nurse shark
LATIN NAME: Ginglymostoma cirratum
LENGTH: Up to 13 ft. (4m.)
WEIGHT: 240 lbs (110kg.)
DIET: Crabs, spiny lobsters, shrimp, sea urchins, squids, and fish
STATUS: Not listed
MUST KNOW: These sharks can live in channels and coral reefs, while the young sharks live in warm shallow waters, such as mangrove swamps.

Nurse sharks are usually seen close to the seabed, where they rest during the day.

▼ Nurse sharks have especially long tails compared with other sharks.

PILES OF SHARKS

Nurse sharks stay close to the seabed in water that is up to 328 ft. (100m) deep. They rest during the day in caves and holes. While they are resting, nurse sharks pump water through their gills. Sometimes, large groups of up to 40 nurse sharks can be seen resting together, all piled up on top of each other. The nurse sharks emerge at night to hunt for animals such as crabs, spiny lobsters, and sea urchins. They suck these animals up off the seabed and then crush them using their strong jaws.

No one is sure how the nurse shark got its name. Some say that the sound it makes sucking up food sounds like a baby suckling milk from its mother. Others think that it comes from an old English word "hurse" that means "seabed shark." Another possibility is that the name comes from "nusse," meaning cat shark, because of the whisker-like barbels the nurse shark has on either side of its mouth.

REPRODUCTION

The females are pregnant for up to six months and give birth to as many as 30 pups in the spring and summer. The newborn sharks are about 12 in. (30cm) long. They stay in shallow water, where they are safe from predators. Nurse sharks can live for 25 years.

APPEARANCE

The nurse shark is yellowish-brown to gray-brown, often with small dark spots. It has strong jaws with rows of small, serrated teeth. Its first dorsal fin is broad and rounded and slightly larger than the second one. Its tail fin is long, almost a quarter of its entire length.

WHERE IN THE WORLD...

This common shark is found along the coast of West Africa and in the western Atlantic, from Rhode Island in North America, south through the Caribbean to Brazil. It is also found in the eastern Pacific, from Baja, California, to Peru.

Arctic Ocean

NORTH AMERICA

U.S.A

EUROPE

ASIA

Pacific Ocean

Atlantic Ocean

AFRICA

SOUTH AMERICA

Indian Ocean

AUSTRALIA

Blue areas show where these sharks may be found.

▲ The rounded snout of the nurse shark bears long barbels.

SHARK BITES

Divers have seen nurse sharks resting with their body raised off the seabed by the fins. This may be a trick to catch crabs that hide under the shark and then get eaten!

PORBEAGLE SHARK

The porbeagle is a type of mackerel shark. It gets its strange name from the old English word "porgh bugel." "Porgh" comes from porpoise, and "bugel" is from the name of the beagle hunting dog.

LIVING IN GROUPS

Porbeagle sharks can live on their own, but usually they live in groups made up of individuals of the same size and sex. These sharks live in both coastal areas and the open ocean, where they can be found to depths of 1,200 ft. (370m)

The porbeagle prefers to live in cold water, where the temperature is less than 57°F (14°C). Normally, cold-water fish are quite sluggish, as their body temperature is the same as the surrounding water, but the porbeagle is a surprisingly active and fast-swimming shark. This is because it can raise the temperature of its body above that of the surrounding water by up to 46°F (8°C) and this helps it stay active. However, this also means that the porbeagle has to eat a lot of food so that it has plenty of energy to keep itself warm.

Porbeagle sharks migrate each year, and this is linked to the temperature of the water. In the winter, when the temperature of the water falls toward freezing, they swim distances of up to 620 mi. (1,000km) into areas of warmer water. They return in the summer when the water warms up.

WHERE IN THE WORLD...

The porbeagle is found in the north Atlantic, Mediterranean, around the southern coast of South America, South Africa, and in the Indian Ocean, Australia, and New Zealand. It is mostly found in the open ocean but sometimes swims into coastal waters.

Blue areas show where these sharks may be found.

REPRODUCTION

Females are pregnant for nine months and give birth to a litter of four to six pups that are 23–30 in. (60-70cm) long. The females can take as long as 12 years before they are ready to breed. Porbeagle sharks live for between 30 and 40 years.

APPEARANCE

Porbeagle sharks have a heavy body that is thick in the middle, with a long, cone-shaped snout, large, round eyes, and large gill slits. They are dark blue to gray in color and pale underneath. Their dorsal fin is dark blue with a patch of white on the rear. Their tail fin is crescent-shaped.

▼ **The porbeagle has narrow, sharp teeth that are ideal for catching slippery fish.**

SHARK FILES

COMMON NAME:	Porbeagle
LATIN NAME:	Lamna nasus
LENGTH:	Up to 12 ft. (4m)
WEIGHT:	507 lbs. (230kg)
DIET:	Fish, especially fast-swimming herring, mackerel, and pilchard, and squids
STATUS:	Vulnerable
MUST KNOW:	The porbeagle has other names, including the Atlantic mackerel shark and the blue dog.

SHARK BITES

Porbeagles can be relatively playful and have been seen tossing around objects that they have found floating in the water.

PORT JACKSON SHARK

The Port Jackson shark is a harmless, slow-moving shark found only in the waters around Australia. It has very distinctive markings and an unusual way of breathing.

SHARK BITES

The eggs take up to 11 months to hatch, and during this time about 90 percent of the unborn pups die.

PUMPING WATER

Most sharks breathe by swimming, when water enters their mouth and passes out over their gills. If they stop swimming, they drown. Port Jackson sharks can eat and breathe at the same time, something that is very unusual for sharks.

The Port Jackson shark pumps water into its gills through its extra large first gill slit and then the water leaves through the other gill slits. This pumping action means that they do not have to swim to breathe, so they can rest on the seabed for long periods of time.

Port Jackson sharks have a territory, or home range, in which they live and hunt. They are active at night, when their prey is also active. During the day, they hide in caves and crevices and under rocks. They use their large back teeth to crush their prey, such as crabs, clams, and sea urchins.

WHERE IN THE WORLD...

The Port Jackson shark is only found in the coastal waters around Australia, in particular along the coast of South Australia. It is usually found in shallow water, but it has been seen at depths of 900 ft. (275 m)

Arctic Ocean

NORTH AMERICA

U.S.A

EUROPE

ASIA

Pacific Ocean

Atlantic Ocean

AFRICA

SOUTH AMERICA

Indian Ocean

AUSTRALIA

Blue areas show where these sharks may be found.

84

▲ The unusual harness-like marking can be clearly seen on this shark.

TEETH AND SAND

The young sharks have different teeth. Their teeth are more pointed, so they eat soft-bodied animals such as worms. When they suck up worms from the sandy seabed, they get a mouthful of sand, but they don't spit out the sand, instead they close their mouth and pump it out through their gill slits.

APPEARANCE

The Port Jackson shark has a blunt head, and its first gill slit is larger than its other four gill slits. It has a distinctive pattern of dark markings that look like a harness. The pattern starts as a band across the snout and then goes along the shark's back to the dorsal fin and down the side of the body. The two dorsal fins are a similar size, with a spine at the front edge.

REPRODUCTION

The females lay eggs. They start laying their eggs in the summer, producing two eggs every two weeks until November. The eggs take about 11 months to hatch.

SHARK FILES

COMMON NAME: Port Jackson shark
LATIN NAME: Heterodontus portusjacksoni
LENGTH: Mostly 2-3 ft. (0.75-1m) but some grow to 5 ft. (1.6m)
WEIGHT: 22-33 lbs. (10-15kg)
DIET: Fish, crustaceans, mollusks, and sea urchins
STATUS: Least concern
MUST KNOW: The shark's front teeth are small, pointed, and very sharp. The teeth at the back are broad and flat, the ideal shape for crushing shells.

SANDBAR SHARK

The sandbar shark likes to stay close to a sandy coast, but it is also called the brown shark because of its color. It is a type of requiem shark and is sometimes seen swimming in harbors.

▼ The sandbar shark has a light nose and pale underside.

CLOSE TO THE SHORE

The large sandbar shark likes coastal habitats such as bays and estuaries where there is a sandy seabed. It prefers shallow water of depths of about 65–210 ft. (20–65m), but it has been known to dive to 660 ft. (200m) or deeper. When it is hunting, it swims close to the seabed looking for prey, such as fish, crabs, and octopus. It may be seen hunting during the day, but usually it is more active at night.

Sandbar sharks make regular journeys, or migrations, each year. During the summer months, they swim either north or south away from the equator and then return in the winter. The male sharks come together and travel in large groups, but the females swim on their own. Not all sandbar sharks migrate. Those that live in the ocean around Hawaii stay in the same warm waters all year round.

REPRODUCTION

The female is pregnant for up to one year. She gives birth to up to 14 pups in shallow water. The pups are about 19–31 in. (50–80cm) long. The number of pups born depends on the size of the female; the larger the female, the more pups she produces.

SHARK FILES

COMMON NAME:	Sandbar shark
LATIN NAME:	Cacharhinus milberti
LENGTH:	Mostly about 6.5 ft. (2m), but can reach 8 ft. (2.5m)
WEIGHT:	About 110–198 lbs. (50–90kg) but the largest known was 260 lbs. (118kg)
DIET:	Fish, mollusks, crabs, shrimp, and octopus
STATUS:	Near threatened
NEED TO KNOW:	The sandbar shark is hunted by larger sharks, such as the tiger and great white shark.

The young sharks stay in shallow water for the first few months or until they are old enough to swim into deeper water where they spend the winter. They return to the shallow waters in the summer. When they are about five years old, they join the adult sharks on their migration.

APPEARANCE

The Sandbar shark has a tall first dorsal fin, and there is a ridge running along its back between its two fins. Like other sharks, the Sandbar's bottom jaw is pressed shut. If the jaw would be opened we would find rows of teeth underneath. The teeth on the upper jaw are large and triangular with serrated edges. Those on the lower jaw have a much narrower base.

WHERE IN THE WORLD...
The sandbar shark is found in tropical and temperate oceans and seas around the world. It is the most abundant large shark in the western Atlantic.

Arctic Ocean

NORTH AMERICA

U.S.A.

EUROPE

Pacific Ocean

Atlantic Ocean

SOUTH AMERICA

Indian Ocean

AFRICA

AUSTRALIA

Blue areas show where these sharks may be found.

SHARK BITES

The main predator of young sandbar sharks is the bull shark.

SHARKS UNDER THREAT

The numbers of sharks around the world are falling rapidly, and more than one-third of sharks are on the brink of extinction, including species such as the whale shark. The main causes for this huge decline are fishing, coastal development, habitat loss such as mangrove clearance, pollution, and climate change.

Shark fins for sale in a market. Finning is threatening the survival of many species of sharks.

CAUGHT FOR MEAT

Small sharks have been fished for their meat for a very long time. The porbeagle and spiny dogfish are among the most popular because their meat is very tasty. However, they have been overfished, and now the spiny dogfish is on the brink of extinction.

SHARK FINNING

Tens of millions of sharks are caught each year just for their fins. The fins are used in shark-fin soup, which is a popular dish in Asian countries. Shark-fin soup is expensive, and it is often served at weddings and other special occasions. The fins have no taste, but they contain a jelly that thickens the soup. Some fins are used in traditional Chinese medicines.

Hammerheads and oceanic white tips are caught only for their fins. These sharks are hauled on to fishing boats, and their fins are sliced off. Their meat has no value, so the finless body is tossed back into the water. Often, the sharks are not dead, so they suffer a slow death in the water. Without fins, they are unable to swim so they are either killed by other sharks or they sink to the seabed where they starve and die.

NETS AND HOOKS

Many more sharks are caught in drift nets. A net can be up to 24 mi. (40km) long and 49 ft. (15m) deep and is left to drift in the sea until the owner returns and hauls it in. The nets catch all sorts of animals, not just the target fish – for example, sharks, seals, whales, and turtles. These other animals are killed or badly injured in the nets. Other sharks die on hooks that are dropped into the ocean on long lines to catch tuna.

This hammerhead shark is just one of thousands of sharks caught each year in fishing nets.

DESTROYED HABITATS

Sharks are also threatened by the loss of their habitat. Mangrove swamps are important nursery areas for young sharks, but these are being cleared to make way for new marinas, hotels, and industry. At sea, the sharks have to cope with pollution caused by oil spills, raw sewage in the water, and trash. Plus, climate change is causing the temperature of the sea to rise. A tiny rise in temperature harms coral, and coral reefs are killed. The fish on the reefs die, too, and this means that there is less food for sharks.

SLOW TO RECOVER

Sharks grow slowly and do not produce large numbers of young, so it takes a long time for shark numbers to increase to replace the millions that are killed. The average size of some of the large sharks is falling, too. Sharks grow throughout their life, so the largest sharks are the oldest ones. However, overfishing means that there are fewer old sharks, so large individuals are becoming rarer.

SHARPNOSE SHARK

The sharpnose shark is a small requiem shark related to the great white sharks. There are two main types of sharpnose sharks, the Atlantic and the Pacific sharpnose.

▼ A Pacific sharpnose swimming in the murky waters off the coast of California.

SHARK FILES

COMMON NAME: Atlantic sharpnose shark
LATIN NAME: Rhizoprionodon terraenovae
LENGTH: 4 ft. (1.1m)
WEIGHT: 15-20 lbs. (7-9kg)
DIET: Worms, crabs, shrimp, mollusks, fish, such as eels, wrass, filefish
STATUS: Least concern
MUST KNOW: Sharpnose sharks have some protection against overfishing in U.S. waters. Each fisherman may only catch one sharpnose shark per fishing trip.

SHALLOW-WATER SHARKS

Sharpnose sharks are found in coastal areas. During the summer months, they like shallow waters, just 40 ft. (12m) or so deep, but in the winter they move to depths of 80 ft. (25m) and more. Sometimes, they are found as deep as 920 ft. (280m). In warmer regions, such as the Gulf of Mexico, sharpnose sharks are present all year round. These sharks are frequently seen in shallow waters off beaches, harbors, and estuaries, but they do not go into fresh water. They live together in groups, and each group consists of sharks of the same sex.

The Pacific sharpnose is a timid shark that lives close to the seabed in waters where visibility is low. As a result, it is rarely seen by divers. Both types of sharpnose sharks are caught in large numbers in coastal waters, and some are caught in commercial fishing nets.

REPRODUCTION

The sharpnose shark is ready to breed when it is about 30 in. (80cm) long, when males are about two years of age, and females a bit older at two and a half to three years. The females are pregnant for 10 to 11 months, and they give birth to up to seven live pups, each between 12-15 in. (30-38cm) long. The young sharks grow quickly in their first few months of life, gaining up to 2 in. (5cm) per month, then their growth rate slows down.

APPEARANCE

The Atlantic sharpnose has a long snout that sticks out far in front of its mouth. Its snout is so long that it makes up 4 percent of its total body length. Its teeth are a triangular shape with serrated edges. These sharks are generally brown or olive-gray to blue-gray in color, and white on the underside.

WHERE IN THE WORLD...

The Atlantic sharpnose occasionally appears as far north as the Bay of Fundy in Canada, but usually it is seen along the coast, from South Carolina to Florida and in the Gulf of Mexico. It is also found off the coast of Brazil. The Pacific sharpnose is found along the eastern Pacific Ocean, from southern California to Peru, and is most abundant in the Sea of Cortex off the coast of Mexico.

Arctic Ocean

NORTH AMERICA

Pacific Ocean

U.S.A

EUROPE

ASIA

Atlantic Ocean

AFRICA

SOUTH AMERICA

Indian Ocean

AUSTRALIA

Blue areas show where sharks may be found.

Sometimes, the adults have a few white spots and a black-edged dorsal and tail fin. The Pacific sharpnose is similar in appearance, although it is gray to copper-brown and slightly larger.

► The extra long snout is a distinctive feature of the Atlantic sharpnose shark.

SIXGILL SHARK

Sixgill sharks are slow-moving sharks that live in deep water. Unlike other sharks, they have six gill slits rather than five. There are two types of sixgill sharks, the bluntnose and the bigeye. The bluntnose, or cow shark, is the more common type.

WHERE IN THE WORLD...

Sixgill sharks are found at depths of between 300–6,600ft. (90–2,000m) in temperate and tropical waters around the world. It is not seen in the Southern Ocean but is found in the Arctic Ocean.

Arctic Ocean

NORTH AMERICA

U.S.A

ASIA

EUROPE

Atlantic Ocean

AFRICA

Pacific Ocean

SOUTH AMERICA

Indian Ocean

AUSTRALIA

Blue areas show where these sharks may be found.

INDEPENDENT SHARK

Sixgill sharks live on their own. They do not stay in deep water all the time. Like many ocean animals, they move between the surface waters and deep water every day, following their prey. During the day, they are found in the deep, but at night they feed near the surface.

Most of the time these sharks are slow movers, but they can move surprisingly fast when they spot prey. They use their saw like teeth to rip flesh from the body of large prey, while smaller prey are caught in the corner of their jaws. Despite their size, the sixgill shark is preyed upon by other predators, especially when they are young. Their main predators are the Steller sea lion, killer whale, and the great white shark.

REPRODUCTION

Male sixgills are ready to breed by the time they are 11 to 14 years old, but females mature more slowly and do not breed until they are 18 to 35 years old. The females may be pregnant for as long as two years. They give birth to large pups, each about 25 - 28 in. (65-70cm) long. Some females produce as many as 100 pups. Sixgills are long-lived sharks, often reaching 80 years of age.

▼ A diver watches a slow-moving sixgill shark. This shark is usually really difficult to find.

APPEARANCE

These sharks have changed very little in appearance in more than 200 million years, so they have more in common with extinct sharks than modern-day sharks that have only five gill slits. Their closest living relatives are the Greenland shark and the dogfish. The sixgill shark is large and powerful with a broad head with small eyes. Its eyes are fluorescent blue-green in color. Its body is gray-brown to dark brown, with a light-colored line along the side of the body. The fins have a lighter-colored edge, and there are dark spots along the sides. Sixgills have only one dorsal fin close to the tail. They have six broad, saw like teeth on each side of the lower jaw. The teeth on the upper jaw are smaller and serrated.

SHARK FILES

COMMON NAME: Sixgill, or cow shark
LATIN NAME: Hexanchus griseus
LENGTH: Most are about 13-15 ft. (4-4.5m) long, the females are larger than the males.
WEIGHT: About, 300lbs. (590kg).
DIET: Crustaceans, such as crabs and mollusks, fish, including hagfish, lampreys, anchov, and salmon
STATUS: Near threatened
MUST KNOW: The females have scars around their gills so scientists think that the males bite them during mating.

▼ This deep-water shark has strange blue-green eyes and six gill slits on each side of its head.

SILVERTIP SHARK

The silvertip shark is a large requiem shark that is found in warm water. It is a powerful and often aggressive shark, especially when there is food around.

PAIRS AND GROUPS

Silvertips are often seen on coral reefs, where they cruise the seaward side of the reefs. They are mainly found in shallow, coastal water, but they will swim as deep as 2,620 ft. (800m). Usually, these sharks live alone or in pairs, but sometimes they form small groups. The adults do not have many predators, but the young sharks may be hunted by large sharks, such as the tiger shark.

REPRODUCTION

The adult sharks are ready to breed when they reach about 5-6 ft. (106-109m) in length. Mating takes place in the summer months. The males can be quite aggressive during mating, and many females have scars, and some even have the top of their dorsal fin bitten off. The females are pregnant for one year when they give birth to between 1 and 11 pups, each of which is about 25 in. (65cm) long.

WHERE IN THE WORLD...
The silvertip shark is found in the warm waters of the Indian and Pacific oceans, along the East African coast and around Madagascar and the Seychelles, from Japan to Australia and along the eastern coast of the Pacific Ocean from Baja, California, to Columbia and around the Galapagos Islands.

Arctic Ocean

NORTH AMERICA

U.S.A

EUROPE

ASIA

Pacific Ocean

Atlantic Ocean

AFRICA

SOUTH AMERICA

Indian Ocean

AUSTRALIA

Blue areas show where these sharks may be found.

▲ Divers have to be careful around the silvertip shark. They keep their disctance from divers but can become excited and dangerous.

GROWING UP

The young sharks stay in the shallows, in particular around reefs where they are safe from predators, such as large sharks. They feed on small reef fish. Once they are larger, the pups are safe to move into deeper water.

APPEARANCE

The shark is dark gray to gray-brown with a hint of bronze. It is white on the underside. It has a pale white band down its sides. Silvertips get their name from the white tips on their fins, including their dorsal and pectoral fins. They have up to 14 teeth in each jaw. The teeth in the upper jaw are large, with a broad base and serrated edges. The teeth in the lower jaw are slightly smaller.

SHARK BITES

The silvertip is often confused with the whitetip reef shark, but the whitetip does not have white tips on its pectoral fins. The gray reef shark is also similar, but it has black tips to its fins.

SHARK FILES

COMMON NAME: Silvertip shark
LATIN NAME: Carcharhinus albimarginatus
LENGTH: Usually 6.5-8ft. (2-2.5m)
Maximum about 10 ft. (3m)
WEIGHT: 350 lbs. (160kg)
DIET: Fish, including eagle rays, wrasse, tuna, small sharks, octopus, and squids
STATUS: Near threatened
MUST KNOW: This is a dangerous shark, and divers need to be careful around it, especially if there is bait in the water.

SILKY SHARK

Most sharks have rough skin that feels like sandpaper and can seriously injure another fish or a diver. However, the silky shark gets its name from the smooth surface of its skin.

SHARK BITES

This shark is nicknamed the net-eater because it attacks tuna nets in the eastern Pacific Ocean.

BIG POPULATION

The silky shark is one of the most common sharks found in open water, with a population of many millions. They spend most of their time at depths of just 160 ft. (50m), but they have been seen to dive to depths of 1,640 ft. (500m). Occasionally, the silky shark moves into shallow coastal waters of just 65.6 ft (20 m) or less in depth.

These sharks are active and can swim 40 mi (60 km) or more per day. They are known to migrate, swimming distances of up to 900 mi (1,440 km).

WARNING DISPLAY

The silky shark is considered to be dangerous, but it does not come into contact with divers very often, as it is found mostly in open oceans. When threatened, the shark performs a warning display before it attacks – it raises its head, arches its back, and drops its tail and pectoral fins.

Silky sharks are fished around the world for their meat and fins. They are caught in nets and on lines with baited hooks. Unfortunately, these sharks have been overfished and are at risk in some parts of the world.

REPRODUCTION

The male sharks are ready to breed by the time they are nine to ten years of age. The females are not ready to mate until they are 12 years old. The females are pregnant for about one year and give birth to between

SHARK FILES

COMMON NAME: Silky shark
LATIN NAME: Carcharhinus falciformis
LENGTH: Mostly around 8 ft (2.5m), but the largest reach 11 ft (3.5m)
WEIGHT: Up to 760 lb (346kg)
DIET: Crabs, squids, fish, such as tuna, mullet, porcupine fish, and mackerel.
STATUS: Near threatened
MUST KNOW: The silky shark is thought to have excellent hearing, which enables it to hear sounds made by its prey from a long way away.

6 and 14 pups. The pups are between 28-33in (70-85cm) long. The young sharks stay in the safety of the shallow water around coral reefs for the first few months of their life and then move out into deeper water. Silky sharks live to between 20 and 25 years of age.

APPEARANCE

The silky shark is long and slender with a rounded snout. Its first dorsal fin slopes back, and it has a small second dorsal fin with a trailing tip. Its pectoral fins are long and narrow. It is dark gray with a bronze sheen, and its underside is white. The teeth on the upper jaw are broad and triangular in shape with large serrations. The lower teeth stand upright and have smooth edges.

▼ The silky shark looks similar to many other requiem sharks, but it has a shiny skin and a rounded first dorsal fin.

WHERE IN THE WORLD...

Silky sharks are found in tropical and subtropical waters across the Atlantic, Indian, and Pacific oceans. In the Atlantic, it is found as far north as Massachusetts and as far south as Brazil, as well as along the west coast of Africa. It is seen in the Red Sea and along the East African and southern Indian coasts. In the Pacific Ocean, it is found from China to New Zealand, Hawaii, and from California to Peru.

Arctic Ocean

NORTH AMERICA

U.S.A.

Atlantic Ocean

EUROPE

ASIA

AFRICA

Pacific Ocean

SOUTH AMERICA

Indian Ocean

AUSTRALIA

Blue areas show where these sharks may be found.

SPINNER SHARK

The name spinner shark comes from the way in which these sharks make spectacular leaps out of the water, spinning around in the air before crashing back into the ocean.

SHARK BITES

Spinner sharks are known to make long migrations each year, moving closer to the shore during the spring and summer months where they feed and breed.

▼ This large, slow-growing shark is under threat from overfishing, and its numbers are falling fast.

SNAPPING UP PREY

Spinner sharks have an unusual way of catching fish. They hunt fish that live in large schools, such as anchovy and sardines. Once they find a school, they swim at full speed into it from below. When they are inside the school, they spin in a spiral, snapping at fish on all sides. Often, spinner sharks swim so fast that they cannot stop themselves from jumping out of the water when they reach the surface. Sometimes, spinner sharks hunt together in small groups.

Spinner sharks are found around the world, where they prefer coastal water less than 100 ft. (30m) deep. Sometimes, however, they are found in water up to 260 ft. (75m) deep. They tend to live close to sandy beaches and banks rather than in clear, open water.

REPRODUCTION

Female spinner sharks are pregnant for up to 15 months. When they are ready to give birth, they swim into shallow coastal water, where they have a litter of up to 15 pups. Each pup is between 23 and 30 in. (60 and 75cm) long. The pups grow quickly, putting on as much as 8in. (20cm) in length in their first six months. Soon, the young are big enough to swim into deeper water.

APPEARANCE

This slender shark has a long, pointed snout and small, round eyes. It has a noticeable notch in its lower jaw. Its first dorsal fin is small with a short rear tip, and its pectoral fins are long and narrow with rounded tips. The shark is gray to bronze with a pale underside. There is a faint pale band running along the sides. Its second dorsal fin, together with the pectoral fins, anal fin, and lower tail fin are tipped in black.

SHARK FILES

COMMON NAME:	Spinner shark
LATIN NAME:	Carcharhinus brevipinna
LENGTH:	Usually around 6.5 ft. (2m), but can grow to 10 ft. (3m)
WEIGHT:	Most are about 132 lbs. (60kg), but up to 198 lbs. (90kg), have been reported
DIET:	Mostly fish, such as sardines, herring, anchovy, tuna, grunt, also squids and octopus
STATUS:	Near threatened
MUST KNOW:	This shark is easily confused with the blacktip shark. The difference is the shape and position of the first dorsal fin. The spinner shark has a more rounded tip that is positioned farther back.

WHERE IN THE WORLD...

The spinner shark is found in the Atlantic Ocean, from North Carolina to Mexico, and Brazil to Argentina. It is found from Spain, along the coast of Africa to Namibia. It is also found in the Mediterranean Sea, Red Sea, and along parts of the eastern coast of Africa to South Africa, including the Seychelles. It is also found along the coast of southern India, Southeast Asia, and Australia, and as far north in the western Pacific Ocean as Japan.

Blue areas show where these sharks may be found.

SAVING SHARKS

The numbers of sharks living in the world's oceans are falling fast, so it's important that people work to save these amazing animals. Unfortunately, many people are scared of sharks, or simply do not like them, so they are not interested in saving them.

Shark tourism brings in money for local people. This diver has paid to have a close encounter with a great white shark.

WHY SAVE SHARKS?

Sharks are crucial to the ecosystem of the oceans. Large sharks, such as great whites, are the top predators in a food chain. This means that they are not hunted by any other animal. When the top predator is killed, the whole food chain is disrupted. For example, if there are not many great white sharks, their prey will increase in number and eat more food. This may lead to food shortages further down the food chain for other marine animals. So protecting sharks helps save other marine animals.

BAN SHARK-FIN SOUP

As many as 200,000 sharks are killed each day just for their meat and fins - that's more than 70 million sharks per year. One of the best ways to save sharks is not to eat shark-fin soup or shark meat. Less demand means fewer sharks are killed. There are campaigns, such as the Bite Back campaign in the U.K. that are working with restaurants and stores to get shark taken off the menu.

Banning shark finning is also important. In the U.S. laws are being passed to ban the finning of sharks in U.S. waters. Once these laws are in place, it will be illegal to land a shark without its fins at any U.S. port. This will make it easier for the authorities to identify the sharks that have been caught and provide better protection for endangered species.

SHARK SANCTUARIES

Two island nations, the Maldives and Palau, have created shark sanctuaries in their waters. There, the sharks are protected and they may not be fished. Also, the export of any shark product has been banned. The governments of these nations realized that sharks were worth much more alive than dead. Tourism, especially diving, brings in a lot of money there and if the sharks disappeared, the divers would go elsewhere.

MARINE RESERVES

Other nations have established marine reserves that protect all the wildlife, not just the sharks. The world's largest marine reserve lies around a group of uninhabited Hawaiian islands in the Pacific Ocean. It covers a massive area of ocean of about 139,000 square mi. (224,000 square km) - that's an area larger than California. The U.K. is planning to create an even larger protected area around the remote Chagos Islands in the Pacific Ocean. The Chagos Islands are unspoiled, and the surrounding waters are probably the cleanest in the world. The coral reefs are home to 1,000 species of fish, including many sharks.

WHAT YOU CAN DO TO SAVE SHARKS:

▸ **Don't** buy any food containing shark meat or fins, such as shark-fin soup
▸ **Buy** fresh seafood and tinned fish that is taken from sources that do not use drift nets that catch and kill sharks
▸ **Don't** buy shark souvenirs such as teeth and jaws
▸ **Join** a conservation group working to save the shark or start one yourself

Visitors watching a whale shark at Georgia Aquarium in the U.S. People change their minds about sharks when they have a chance to watch them at close quarters.

SMOOTHHOUND SHARK

Smoothhound sharks are a group of 25 small sharks that are very active but harmless. Their Latin name, *Mustelus*, means weasel.

LIVING WITH OTHER SHARKS

Smoothhound sharks live in groups with other small sharks, such as the leopard shark. They are active at night, when they are commonly seen in shallow waters around coasts, at depths of about 7–150 ft. (2–45m).

SHARK FILES

COMMON NAME:	Gray smoothhound
LATIN NAME:	*Mustelus californicus*
LENGTH:	About 4-5.5 ft. (1.15-1.65m), females are larger than males
WEIGHT:	22-33 lbs. (10-15kg)
DIET:	Ghost shrimp, mollusks, worms, small fish, such as herring
STATUS:	Not listed
MUST KNOW:	The Gulf smoothhound is closely related and looks very similar to the Florida smoothhound.

SHARK BITES

There are some very rare albino smoothhounds that are completely white.

▼ This grey smoothhound looks very similar to a Gulf smoothhound but has a smaller dorsal fin.

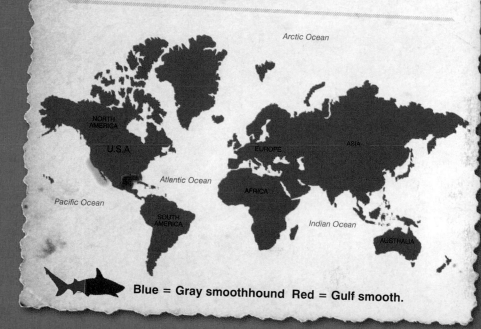

◄ Gray smoothhound sharks are often found in bays and along rocky shores.

These small sharks prey on a variety of animals such as shrimp, worms, and crustaceans. Their teeth are flat and plate like, the ideal shape for crushing tough shells. They also catch small fish, such as herring and menhaden. Smoothhounds are preyed upon by larger sharks, such as the dusky, blacktip, and hammerhead sharks.

Smoothhounds are fished commercially, and scientists are concerned that their numbers are falling to low levels. These sharks are slow to reproduce, and they only produce a few young, so their numbers will take many years to recover.

NEW SPECIES

In 2003, a new species of smoothhound was discovered by a marine biologist working in the Sea of Cortez, off the coast of Mexico. He called it *Mustelus hacat*. It is dark gray in color, about 5 ft (1.5m) long, and with white markings on the tips and edges of its fins.

REPRODUCTION

Female smoothhound sharks give birth to live young. The females are ready to breed when they are about 28–30 in. (70–75cm) long. They are pregnant for 10 to 11 months and give birth to their

young in the waters off the coast of California. The litter size is between one and five pups, and each pup is about 8–12 in (20–30cm) long. Smoothhounds only live for six to nine years.

APPEARANCE

The gray smoothhound, as the name suggests, is gray-brown on top and pale gray underneath with no spots or stripes. Its body is long, and slender and it has large oval eyes. Its second dorsal fin is large. The Gulf smoothhound is a similar color with a pale underside, but its first dorsal fin is large with a rounded tip.

SWELLSHARK

The swellshark is a type of catshark that lives along the Pacific coastline of North and South America. Its odd name comes from the way that it can swell up to appear much bigger when it is threatened.

IN A PILE

Swellsharks are often seen along the coast, where their favorite habitat is rocky shores with a lot of seaweed. However, they are also found in much deeper water. Swellsharks rest during the day, hiding in crevices and caves, and then come out at night to hunt for fish and crustaceans. Often a large group of swellsharks use the same hiding place, lying on top of each other in a pile.

SEARCH FOR FOOD

These sharks have lots of different ways of catching prey. Sometimes, they lie on the seabed and wait for their prey to pass close by and then grab it. At other times, they lie on the seabed with their mouth wide open and simply wait for prey to swim inside! Swellsharks are small, so they are preyed upon by larger predators. They have a smart way of defending themselves. When they are threatened, they swallow lots of water so that their body swells up, sometimes doubling in size. This makes it very difficult for the predator to eat them.

WHERE IN THE WORLD...
Found in the eastern Pacific Ocean, from California south to Chile. It prefers warm tropical and subtropical water. It ranges in depth from just 16 ft. (5 m) near the coast to depths of up to 4,920 ft. (1,500m), where the water is very cold.

Arctic Ocean

Atlantic Ocean

Pacific Ocean

Indian Ocean

Blue areas show where these sharks may be found.

REPRODUCTION

Swellsharks are egg-layers. The females lay two green- or amber-colored eggs. The egg case is a flattened shape, about 1–3 in. (2.5–7cm) in size.

The tendrils at the corners of the egg case wrap around rocks on the seabed so the eggs are not carried away. The eggs take about 7–12 months to hatch, depending on the temperature of the water; they take longer when the water is cool. The newly hatched pups are about 6 in. (15cm) long. These sharks are at risk because they produce so few eggs, and each egg takes a long time to hatch. If they are overfished for their meat, the numbers of swellsharks take many decades to recover.

APPEARANCE

Swellsharks have a broad head with a short snout and large mouth that contains about 60 small teeth. Their large, oval eyes are a golden color. Their brown body is covered with black dots, and their fins are light brown with dark patches. The dorsal fins are rounded at the tip.

▼ **This swellshark is resting close to the seabed, above a group of purple sea urchins.**

TIGER SHARK

The tiger shark is one of the most dangerous sharks in the ocean. It is incredibly aggressive, especially when there is food in the water. Like its namesake, the tiger, it is an expert hunter.

MURKY WATER

The tiger shark is a common shark in tropical and warm temperate waters. It is found in shallow coastal waters as well as in ocean water to 460 ft. (140m) deep. It has even been found at depths of 2,950. ft (900m). It likes areas where the water is churned up by fresh water running into the sea, such as estuaries and harbors. The murky water makes it more difficult for prey animals to spot the tiger shark when it is approaching them. Tiger sharks live on their own. They rest during the day and hunt at night and eat almost anything, from small invertebrates, such as crabs and mollusks to birds, turtles, and mammals, such as seals and dolphins. Tiger sharks will even eat trash floating in the water, which can harm them.

REPRODUCTION

A female tiger shark is pregnant for up to 16 months and gives birth to live young.

SHARK BITES

The tiger shark is on Greenpeace's Seafood Red list. This is a list of fish that are being caught at unsustainably high levels but are still sold in stores. Consumers should avoid these fish.

WHERE IN THE WORLD...

Tiger sharks are found in the tropical waters of the Atlantic, Indian, and Pacific oceans. They are found close to the equator during the winter months, but during the summer they move away, swimming as far north as Japan and south to New Zealand.

Arctic Ocean

NORTH AMERICA

U.S.A

EUROPE

ASIA

Atlantic Ocean

Pacific Ocean

AFRICA

SOUTH AMERICA

Indian Ocean

AUSTRALIA

Blue areas show where these sharks may be found.

▲ A tiger shark makes very small movements when it swims, and its tall dorsal fin helps it turn around quickly.

The litter size varies, from just 10 pups to as many as 80. Each pup is about 20–28.5 in. (50–70cm) long. Tiger sharks live for about 25–27 years.

APPEARANCE

The tiger shark gets its name from the dark bars on its body. It has a broad, flat head, with a snout that is shorter than width of its mouth. Its slender body ends in a long, pointed tail fin. Tiger sharks are blue-gray to black with a pale white to yellow underside. Young tiger sharks have mottled patterns of blotches on their upper surface. As they age, the markings form bars along the top and sides of the body. The dark bars on the top fade with age but remain along the sides and tail.

SHARK FILES

COMMON NAME: Tiger shark
LATIN NAME: Galeocerdo cuvier
LENGTH: Usually 9.8–13.9 ft. (3–4.25m) largest reported to be 5.5 m (180ft)
WEIGHT: 840–1410 lbs (380–640kg)
DIET: Crabs, squids, fish, turtles, birds, and seals
STATUS: Near threatened
MUST KNOW: Native Hawaiians consider the tiger shark to be sacred, and they believe that its eyes have special seeing powers.

▲ The distinctive bar markings along the side of this adult tiger shark can be clearly seen.

WHALE SHARK

▼ Whale sharks swim slowly through the world's oceans, feeding on plankton and small fish. They do not seem to mind divers swimming alongside them.

The awesome whale shark is the world's largest fish. It may be huge, but it is harmless, and its tiny teeth are not used for feeding at all.

BIG MOUTH

Whale sharks feed close to the surface of the water, where swarms of plankton gather. To feed, the shark opens its mouth and extends its jaws. Then it sucks hard to fill its mouth with water. It closes its mouth and pushes the water through the gills, where any food is trapped and removed.

When they are feeding in an area with a lot of plankton, whale sharks swing their head from side to side, sucking in water as they go. When they sense that there are few plankton in the water, they turn around and go back again.

REPRODUCTION

Little is known about the reproduction of the whale shark. In 1995, scientists finally found proof that whale sharks give birth to live young. A female whale was found with 300 unborn pups inside her. The pups were about 24 in. (60cm) long. Scientists believe that whale sharks are not ready to breed until they are about 30 years old. They live for at least 60, possibly 100, years.

Whale sharks are killed for their meat and fins. Unfortunately, their meat sells for a high price, so fishermen hunt out this shark. As many as 100 are killed in the waters around Taiwan each year.

SHARK FILES

COMMON NAME: Whale shark
LATIN NAME: *Rhincodon typus*
LENGTH: Up to 66 ft. (20m)
WEIGHT Up 22 tons or more
DIET: Planktonic plants and animals, krill, shrimp, small fish, sometimes squids
STATUS: Vulnerable
MUST KNOW: The large number of whale sharks that gather off the Ningaloo Reefs in Western Australia have become an important tourist attraction for the area.

WHERE IN THE WORLD...

Whale sharks swim long distances, so they are found in tropical and warm temperate waters around the world. They are usually seen in the open ocean, but they come close to the shore to feed and may even swim into harbors, estuaries, and lagoons. They have been seen at depths of 2,300 ft. (700m).

Arctic Ocean

Atlantic Ocean

Pacific Ocean

Indian Ocean

AUSTRALIA

Blue areas show where these sharks may be found.

SHARK BITES

Whale sharks have 300 rows of tiny teeth, each just a small hook. They are not used for feeding.

OCEANIC WHITETIP SHARK

▼ The shark's wing-like pectoral fin can be seen clearly in this photograph.

The whitetip shark hunts alone far out at sea. It is responsible for more attacks on people than all the other types of sharks put together.

▼ The whitetip shark has a rounded dorsal fin with a white spot at the tip.

SHARK BITES

During the Second World War, a ship carrying 1,000 men was sunk by a German U-boat submarine off the coast of South Africa. Many were killed by whitetip sharks that gathered around the shipwreck, and fewer than 200 survived.

SWIMMING WITH WHALES

The whitetip shark is active day and night. It swims slowly through the water and travels long distances in its search for food, as prey animals are scarce in the open ocean. Usually, they are spotted in deep water away from land, but they do hunt in shallower water, often around oceanic islands. Often, whitetips are seen in the company of pilot whales. Scientists are not sure why, but it could be due to the fact that the pilot whales are good at finding prey animals, such as squid, a favorite food of the whitetip shark.

Groups of whitetips are sometimes seen around food sources, such as whale carcasses. Sometimes, the presence of food causes them to go into a feeding frenzy. When this happens, the sharks go into an uncontrollable rage. They thrash around in the water, taking bites out of the food and anything else in their way, even each other.

REPRODUCTION

Whitetip sharks are ready to breed when they are about six years old. Female whitetip sharks give birth to live young after a pregnancy of about one year. The litter size is between 1 and 15 pups, and each pup is about 24 in. (60cm) long. These sharks live for about 22 years.

APPEARANCE

This is a requiem shark, but it has a shorter body than other requiem sharks, with a large, rounded first dorsal fin and very long pectoral fins that look like paddles. It has a short head, blunt nose, and small round eyes. Its body is gray-brown with a pale, almost white, underside. It gets its name from the white tips on its fins.

SHARK FILES

COMMON NAME: Oceanic whitetip shark
LATIN NAME: Carchinrhinus longimanus
LENGTH: About 10-13 ft. (3-4m)
WEIGHT: Up to 370 lbs. (170kg)
DIET: Fish, such as barracuda, marlin, and tuna, as well as turtles, birds, squids, and crustaceans. It will also feed on dead animals in the water.
STATUS: Vulnerable
MUST KNOW: Whitetip sharks may lift their nose out of the water to sniff the air to seek out prey.

WHERE IN THE WORLD...

The whitetip shark is found around the world in tropical and subtropical waters where the water temperature is 70°F (21°C) and above. It is found as far north as the coast of Maine in the U.S. and as far south as Argentina and South Africa.

Blue areas show where these sharks may be found.

SHARK RELATIVES

There are some strange-looking fish that are close relatives of sharks and are often mistaken for them. They have some of the same characteristics as sharks, but they are not quite sharks.

The white-spotted shovelnose guitarfish has a flattened head, typical of all guitarfish.

The sawfish uses its amazing saw as a rake to find prey in the mud and to slash at moving fish.

GUITARFISH

The guitarfish has a strange shape. It looks like a cross between a shark and a ray. Its head and the front end of its body are flattened and elongated, and its paired fins are fused to the side of its body and stick out like wings. The back end of its body looks like a shark with two dorsal fins, a long tail, and tail fin. It grows to about 6.5 ft. (2m) in length.

Guitarfish live on the seabed in shallow tropical and temperate water. They often bury themselves in the sand or mud and wait for prey to pass close by. They feed on crabs and other crustaceans, as well as small fish. There are a number of different types of guitarfish, including the shovelnose and the bowmouth guitarfish.

The females swim into shallow water to give birth to live young. There are usually between two and four pups in a litter. The young guitarfish stay in the shallow water until they are adults. They bury themselves in the sand to hide from predators, such as others sharks.

Guitarfish are closely related to rays. Rays are cartilaginous fish, just like sharks, which means that they have a skeleton made mainly from a substance called cartilage rather than bone. Cartilage is more rubbery and not as brittle as bone. The guitarfish body is flattened from top to bottom, and their large, triangular pectoral fins look like wings. Their mouth and gills are on the underside of their body.

SAWFISH

Sawfish look like sharks, but they are more closely related to rays. Sawfish are large fish,

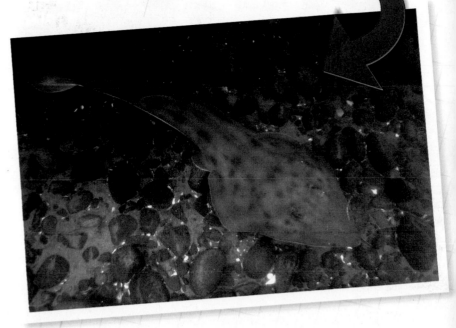

The mottled pattern of the shovelnose guitarfish provides perfect camouflage when it rests on the seabed.

and some grow to lengths of more than 18 ft. (5.5m). Their most distinguishing feature is their incredibly long saw-edged snout. The snout is covered in ampullae of Lorenzini, which means that it can detect animals buried in the mud.

Once the sawfish detects an animal buried in mud or sand, it digs it up with its snout and then kills it using the sharp saw edge of its snout. Sawfish like the tropical waters of the Atlantic and Indian oceans. They prefer shallow, muddy water and will swim into freshwater rivers. All the sawfish are critically endangered, as they are hunted for their saws.

A female sawfish gives birth to up to eight pups. The pups are born with a rubbery covering over their saw so that their mother is not injured during the birth. The covering drops off after a few days. The young sawfish grow very slowly and do not reach adult size until they are about ten years old. They live for about 30 years. Their slow rate of reproduction means that they do not recover very quickly from being hunted and overfished.

WHITETIP REEF SHARK

The whitetip reef shark is one of the most common species of sharks found on coral reefs. It is often seen with other sharks, such as the blacktip reef and gray reef sharks.

▼ The distinctive white tips on the dorsal and tail fins identify this shark as a whitetip reef shark.

SHARK FILES

COMMON NAME: Whitetip reef shark
LATIN NAME: Triaenodon obesus
LENGTH: Mostly up to 5 ft. (1.5m), the largest 7.5 ft. (2.3m)
WEIGHT: 40 lbs. (18kg)
DIET: Crabs, spiny lobsters, and octopus
STATUS: Near threatened
MUST KNOW: They have favorite resting places and may return to the same spot every day for many years.

RESTING IN CAVES

During the day, the whitetip reef shark likes to rest in caves and under ledges. Sometimes, they rest together in groups, lying side by side or even piled up on top of each other.

Whitetip reef sharks tend to hunt in a particular area of reef about 0.2 square mi. (0.5 square km) and rarely travel farther afield. They prefer shallow water but can be found as deep as 980 ft. (300m).

The sharks hunt at night. Usually, they hunt on the seaward side of a reef, but they may swim into lagoons and channels where there are fast-flowing currents. Groups of whitetip reef sharks have been seen hunting together. The group works together, slowly going over a certain area of the reef, flushing animals, such as crabs and lobsters, from their hiding places.

REPRODUCTION

Whitetip reef sharks are ready to breed when they are about eight years old and are about 3 ft. (1m) long. The female sharks give birth to live young after one year of pregnancy. Each litter consists of between one to five pups, each about 24 in. (60cm) long. They live for about 25 years.

APPEARANCE

This small shark has a slender body with a short, broad head. Curled flaps of skin hang down from its nostrils. The first dorsal fin is placed quite far down its back, and the second dorsal fin is large. They get their name from the white tips of their dorsal, anal, and tail fins. The pectoral fins are triangular in shape. This shark is gray-brown with small dark spots and a pale underside.

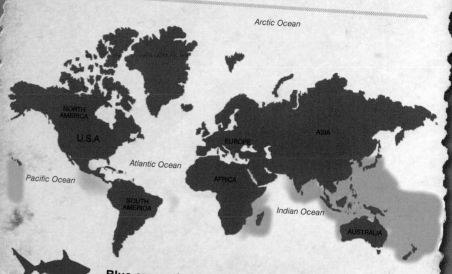

WHERE IN THE WORLD...

Whitetip reef sharks are found in tropical waters, especially near coral reefs, in the Indian and Pacific oceans. They are found from the Red Sea south to South Africa and along the coastline of Southeast Asia to China, and across Asia to Australia and Hawaii. They are also seen around the Galapagos Islands and along the Pacific coast of Central America.

Arctic Ocean

NORTH AMERICA

U.S.A

EUROPE

ASIA

Atlantic Ocean

Pacific Ocean

AFRICA

SOUTH AMERICA

Indian Ocean

AUSTRALIA

Blue areas show where these sharks may be found.

◄ A group of whitetip reef sharks hunting for fish among rocks on the seabed.

SHARK BITES

When hunting, these sharks have been seen to wiggle their bodies under ledges and in crevices and then they twist to break off the coral in order to get at their prey.

WOBBEGONG SHARK

▼ A tasseled wobbegong lies in wait on the seabed, its frill of skin flaps breaking up its outline so that it's more difficult to spot.

The wobbegong gets its weird name from an Australian Aboriginal word, which means shaggy beard. The "beard" is a row of skin flaps that hang down around its mouth.

GREAT CAMOUFLAGE

Wobbegongs belong to a group of carpet sharks that include the banded, spotted, and tasseled wobbegong. The way that the wobbegong looks helps them hide from predators and hunt for prey. Their flattened shape, markings across their body and seaweed like flaps around the mouth provide camouflage for the shark when it is resting on the seabed.

To catch prey, the wobbegong lies motionless on the seabed. When prey comes too close, it opens its jaws and sucks the unsuspecting animal into its large mouth. Sometimes, the sharks allow an animal to nibble their skin flaps before they make their move. At night, the wobbegongs swim over the seabed looking for prey such as crabs, octopus, and small sharks.

WHERE IN THE WORLD...

Wobbegongs are found in the western Pacific Ocean, in particular around the coasts of Australia and Japan. Some are found in the South China Sea. They live in coastal habitats. Tasseled wobbegongs are usually found on coral reefs to depths of 130 ft. (40m). Spotted wobbegongs are seen around coral reefs, under piers, and on rocky seabeds, and in shallow water to depths of 330 ft. (100m).

Blue areas show where these sharks may be found.

REPRODUCTION

Female wobbegongs give birth to live young. Scientists believe that the females nourish the unborn pups by producing a milk-like substance that is soaked up by the pups through their skin. The spotted wobbegong has up to 37 pups in a litter, while the tasseled wobbegong produces about 20 pups. The pups are about 8 in. (20cm) long when they are born. No one is sure how long these sharks live for.

APPEARANCE

Wobbegongs have a flattened, broad body. The tasseled wobbegong has a distinctive fringe of skin flaps from the tip of its snout to the base of its pectoral fins. Its body is pale brown with a pattern of dark lines and spots. The spotted Wobbegong has a similar shape, but it has far fewer skin flaps. This shark is pale yellow to brown with a series of dark saddles down the center of its back that are surrounded by small, white circular marks. It is larger than the tasseled wobbegong.

SHARK FILES

COMMON NAME:	Tasseled wobbegong
LATIN NAME:	Eucrossorhinus dasypogon
LENGTH:	Up to 4 ft. (1.3m)
DIET:	Crabs, octopus, and small fish
STATUS:	Near threatened
MUST KNOW:	Wobbegongs are not dangerous, but they do not like being stepped on – when this happens, they bite, causing nasty injuries.

SHARK BITES

The spotted wobbegong is fished in Australia, and its meat, known as flake, is used in fish and chip meals. The skin is used to make a patterned leather.

▼ A spotted wobbegong lies perfectly camouflaged under a rock.

ZEBRA SHARK

The name zebra shark comes from the white stripes seen on the young sharks. However, the adults have spots and for this reason they are also called leopard sharks - but they are not the same as the leopard sharks on page 72!

FLEXIBLE BODY

Zebra sharks live close to the seabed in shallow coastal waters, up to depths of 200 ft. (60m). Often, they are seen on or close to coral reefs. These solitary sharks spend much of the day resting on the seabed and are active at night when they hunt for crabs, spiny lobsters, mollusks, and fish. The zebra shark has a particularly flexible body and can wiggle into small crevices and under ledges in its search for prey.

The zebra shark is preyed upon by larger sharks and other types of predatory fish as well as seals.

In parts of its range, the numbers of zebra shark have fallen dramatically. This is mostly due to overfishing because the fins are used in shark-fin soup and the liver is dried to make some Chinese medicines.

SHARK BITES

A zebra shark will often have remoras, or sharksuckers clinging to its mouth or nose. Remoras use their large sucker to grip to the shark's skin so they can feed on leftover food and parasites on the skin.

WHERE IN THE WORLD...

Zebra sharks are found in the tropical and warm temperate regions of the Indian and Pacific oceans, from the Red Sea and East Africa, across to Southeast Asia, to southern Japan and Australia. They are especially abundant in the waters around northern Australia.

Blue areas show where these sharks may be found.

▲ This is an adult zebra shark with spots rather than stripes. Zebra sharks have a distinctive ridge running along the side of their body.

SHARK FILES

COMMON NAME: Zebra shark
LATIN NAME: Stegostoma fasciatum
LENGTH: 8-11 ft. (2.5-3.5m)
DIET: Crabs, shrimp, mollusks, and small fish
STATUS: Vulnerable
MUST KNOW: An all-white or albino female zebra shark was found in the Pacific Ocean in 1973. Albino animals are very rare, as the coloring makes them more visible to predators.

REPRODUCTION

Zebra sharks are egg-layers. They are ready to breed when they are about 5.5 ft. (2m) long. The females lay large, dark purple egg cases that are about 7 in. (17cm) long and 3 in. (8cm) wide. Long, hair-like fibers attach the egg case to rocks and seaweed to stop them from drifting away. The young pups are 8–14 in. (20–36cm) long when they hatch. The zebra shark lives for about 25 years.

APPEARANCE

The adults have a yellowish-brown body with dark brown leopard-like spots. There are several very obvious skin ridges running along the length of their body. Their pectoral fins are large and rounded, and their two spineless dorsal fins lie close together. Their tail fin is almost as long as the rest of their body. The young zebra sharks look very different from the adults. They are dark brown to black with white stripes and blotches. The colors start to change when the shark is about 28 in. (70cm) long.

FACTS AND FEATS

- **The largest shark** in the oceans today is the huge whale shark, which can grow to a massive 52 ft. (16m) long. The second largest is the basking shark, which is shorter at around 40 ft. (12m).

- **The largest predatory** shark is the great white at 20 ft. (6m).

- **The smallest living sharks** such as the dwarf lantern shark of the deep ocean, the spined pygmy shark and the pygmy ribbontail catshark, are between 6–8 in. (16–20cm) long. They are smaller than many newborn shark pups.

- **The fastest swimmer** is the mako shark, which can move through the water at speeds of 20 mph (32kph). Some scientists believe that these sharks can swim as fast as 60 mph (100kph), but this has not been proved. Sometimes, mako sharks leap out of the water and end up in boats.

- **Sharks never stop growing**, they get gradually longer each year and this means that the largest sharks are also the oldest sharks.

- **Many sharks die** before they are fully grown.

- **Most sharks live** less than 25 years, but there are some exceptions. The spiny dogfish may live for 100 years, while scientists believe that the Greenland shark may live for more than 200 years.

This diver is watching lemon sharks in the Bahamas, an area where lemon sharks have been studied by scientists for many years.

- **The great white shark** is at greater risk of becoming extinct than the tiger. Other sharks at even greater risk of extinction are Harrison's deep-sea dogfish (also called the dumb gulper shark), the striped dogfish, several species of angel sharks, and many of the river sharks, such as the Ganges shark and the New Guinea river shark.

- **Hundreds of years ago**, sword-makers in Germany and Japan wrapped the handles of the swords that they made in shark skin to give a better grip.

- **Shark skin** can be made into a tough, long-lasting leather once the denticles are removed.

- **More people die** from bee stings each year than from shark attacks.

The largest-ever shark to have lived was Megalodon, which terrorized the oceans 15 million years ago. This huge shark may have reached 66 ft. (20m) long, with teeth the size of an adult human hand.

- **The very first sharks** appeared on Earth about 400 million years ago - that's a 100 million years before the dinosaurs.

- **Scientists can identify individual** whale sharks from the pattern of marks on the skin behind their gills and from scars. This helps them learn more about these giant sharks as they swim across the oceans.

- **Wobbegong sharks** are very flexible, and they can even bite their own tails. If you pick up a wobbegong, it can bend its body and bite your hand!

Tiger sharks are often nicknamed the "swimming trash cans" because of all the strange objects that have been found in their stomach, including nails, drums, tires, clothing, and even an unexploded torpedo.

GLOSSARY

ALBINO all–white, lacking color

AMPULLAE OF LORENZINI sense organs found in the snout of sharks that enable sharks to find their prey

BARBEL whisker–like sensory flap that hangs from the nostrils of many sharks

CAMOUFLAGE coloring that blends in with the background

CARTILAGE the material that forms the skeleton of a shark

CRUSTACEAN invertebrate animal that has a heavy outer covering, or exoskeleton, and jointed legs, for example, crabs and lobsters

DORSAL FIN fin found on the back of a fish

EELGRASS type of plant that has long, grass–like leaves, found growing in shallow water

ELECTRORECEPTION ability of sharks to pick up electrical signals produced by other animals

ENDANGERED under threat of becoming extinct

ESTUARY place where a river enters the sea, with shallow water, mudflats, and sand banks

EQUATOR the imaginary line around the center of Earth

EXTINCT no longer living or in existence

FOSSIL the remains of an animal or plant that lived thousands or millions of years ago

GILL the organ responsible for picking up oxygen from the water

GILL SLIT opening to the gills, through which water passes out

INVERTEBRATE animal that lacks a backbone, for example, insects, worms, and mollusks

▼ The gray reef shark is one of the most common sharks found in the Indian and Pacific oceans.

KELP BED place where kelp (a type of brown seaweed) grows like a forest in shallow water

LOBE rounded part of a fin

MARINA a dock for yachts and small pleasure boats

MOLLUSK invertebrate animal, with a soft body that is often enclosed within a shell, for example, snails, clams and mussels. Octopus and squids are also mollusks and they lack an external shell

PAIRED FINS the pectoral and pelvic fins that occur in pairs

PARASITE an organism, such as an animal or plant, that lives on or in another organism, feeding on it and causing it harm

PECTORAL FIN one of a pair of fins found just behind the head

PELVIC FIN one of a pair of fins found toward the tail

PREDATOR an animal that hunts and eats other animals

PREY animals that are hunted and eaten by other animals

REQUIEM a species, or type, of shark that includes the dusky, lemon, sharpnose, and tiger sharks

SEAWARD facing the sea

SNOUT fleshy part of the head above the mouth, also called the nose

SPIRACLE hole behind the eye seen in some sharks that allows water to pass to the gills

STAGHORN CORAL a type of coral that has long branches that look like antlers

STREAMLINED shaped like a torpedo, a sleek body that slips easily through the water

SUBTROPICAL relating to zones that lie to the north and south of the tropics, which have a warm climate with seasons

TROPICAL relating to the tropics, a zone that lies around the equator with a very warm and often humid climate

TEMPERATE zones where the climate is moderate, neither too hot or too cold, with seasons lying between the subtropics and the polar regions

VERTEBRATE animal that has a backbone, for example, fish, amphibians, reptiles, birds and mammals

▼ The lemon shark is a type of requiem shark.

INDEX

ACKNOWLEDGEMENTS

Credits

Front Cover: Brandon Cole/Visuals Unlimited, Inc./Getty Images
Back Cover: iStockphoto/ThinkStock
Title page: Comstock/ThinkStock
Jacket Flaps: Comstock/ThinkStock (Back Flap),
iStockphoto/ThinkStock
Endpapers: iStockphoto/ThinkStock (Front),
Hemera/ThinkStock (Back)

Albert Kok 29, 109
Corbis Norbert Wu 43, Sealife Park 54,55
Ecoscene / John Lewis 13,40, John Liddiard 60
Ecoscene Chinch Gryniewicz 40
Ecoscene / Reinhard Dirscherl 21, 38, 51, 64, 65,80,88 96,97,
110,111, 116, 117, 121, 122
Ecoscene / Phillip Colla 24, 31,63 99,
Ecoscene / Papilio / Robert Pickett 88
Ecoscene /VWPics / Andy Murch 8,13,14,15,16,23,25,39,44,45,
46,47,58,59,74,75,83,85,86, 87, 91,92,93, 95, 100, 104,105, 107,
114,115,119
Ecoscene /VWPics / Kike Calvo 37, 56, 79, 90,
Ecoscene /VWPics / Andre Seale 36, 42,41,69
Ecoscene /VWPics / Mark Conlin 11, 19, 32, 66,73

Ecoscene /VWPics / David Fleetham 95
VWPics / Masa Ushioda 26,27

Shutterstock 81, Brandylet 63, CBPics 124, Teguh Tirtaputra
118, Mark Higgins 18, Ciurzynski 28,Fiona Ayerst title, 5, 7,
30, 71,125, Ian Scott 30, Rich Carey 35, 80, Scott 53, 61, 123,
Folsom 57, Browne 78, Undersea Discoveries 123,
Jim Capaldi 48
Steven Kuhn 18
Matthew Field 73
NOAA 17
Dmitry Bogdanov 53
Masur 52
Zac Wolf 103
Zul Rosle 12
Ian Norwood 86
Nature pl Bruce Rasner Doug Perrine
Istock 79